Untold histor

based on a true

The Bridgetower

Chronicles

Told by Eileen Christie

HOUSE OF SOLOMON

Contents

Chapter 1.

Yohannes' Story, Abyssinia

I was born into captivity, but not in the way some would perhaps think. I am an Abyssinian Prince, and it is a custom in my country that all male heirs to the imperial throne are confined to a castle until we are called forth to replace the Emperor. My father is Prince Yohannes and has spent his life behind the castle walls. He strongly opposes this custom, which began in 1636 when our ancestor, Emperor Fasilides, discovered his eldest son, Dawit, was planning a revolt. He was so enraged, he banished him to his castle in the city of Gondar, along with his younger sons, and proclaimed that all male heirs would remain in the confines of the castle until the day they were called upon. Although our castles are exquisite like beautiful palaces and we are waited on hand and foot by loyal servants, we want for nothing other than to go beyond our castle walls. My father accepted his fate, but he refused to accept this was to be mine too. He wishes for nothing more than for me to go out into the world.

For months, there had been whispers of a Dutch sea captain coming to visit our palace; the hushed whispers were not to fall upon the ears of children whose loose little lips had the power to sink ships.

I will always remember the day the Dutch sea captain arrived; the sound of the palace doors swinging open and slamming into the stone walls rippled through the grand hall. I remember how excited we felt to have a European visitor.

He strutted in, bringing with him an air of arrogance, a clear indicator that he was a well-travelled and refined gentleman. He was quickly shown to my fathers' quarters, where hushed conversation took place behind the heavy wooden door. I was soon to learn that these conversations were focused on making quick arrangements for my departure.

My servants had begun packing my garments, tying them into large bundles and taking them from my quarters. I had not spoken to my father and hoped my servants had made a mistake, while at the same time, I prayed my father would change his mind by the morning.

However, late into that very night, I remember being woken and told to get dressed. The eerie silence was broken only by my soft footsteps as I made my way outside, led only by the light of the pale moon. I could see my father standing by the gate, looking out at the night sky. As I approached, he turned around and gave me a soft, comforting smile that made my stomach churn. The gentle sadness in his eyes gave it all away. This was farewell.

"You, my son...," I remember him telling me, "are the brightest prince in this kingdom. You are to be taken to Europe to be educated in the ways of the world. You will learn about the arts, science, and philosophy. You will see things I have only heard about. One day, you will return a great man ready to lead and teach our people. Far too many generations of our family have been confined behind castle walls; you will be the one to break this cycle."

I was fourteen years old. I did not quite understand the gravity and responsibility of the task my father was giving me. I already had the best education and worked hard. I could speak English, as well as my native Abyssinian. The gut-wrenching fear of realising I would be leaving the only home I knew, my country, my family, consumed my mind.

My father was never an outwardly emotional man. He was, however, a pinnacle of masculine energy and strength. But that night, after our final goodbyes, the sea captain, myself and a small number of servants started our journey to the array of camels already prepared for the voyage to the Red Sea, I was sure I saw his eyes misting. As I looked up at my father, the mist seemed to clear as quickly as it had emerged. That was forever my last memory of my father.

The sea captain was to be my chaperone; the gold and diamonds my father had rewarded him with were, indeed, a sight to behold. Once we reached the Red Sea, I was led to a grand schooner. It was unlike anything I had ever seen before, and the captain had arranged for my cabin to be laden with goods required for the lavish lifestyle I was accustomed too.

The sea was exceptionally calm as we set sail, gentle enough for me to venture out onto the deck. I had spent all my life in the castle high up on a mountain, so to be surrounded by so much water was an unnatural feeling. It took days for my stomach to stop swaying with each gentle wave that rocked the boat. Initially, the captain was pleasant and told me stories of amazing faraway countries with animals I could not imagine and people with strange traditions, unlike any of my own.

But as the days turned into weeks, the mood on the schooner gradually cooled even more than the rough sea wind around us. I was confused when previous acceptable behaviour became a crime followed by brutal punishment. My chaperone, whom my father had trusted, had suddenly become my captor. My servants tried their best to nurse my wounds as well as their own, but the raw bleeding cuts left behind scars that embodied the ones eternally left in our minds.

Soon, we were taken from our quarters and put into the hull of the ship. I lost track of time, unable to see the outside world. Night and day merged into one seemingly never-ending period. When the loud noise of the ship anchoring jolted our surroundings, it was like being woken from a trance. Suddenly,

I felt warmer and it was almost as if I could feel strength coming back into my body. But I suppose that is what hope does.

Anxiously, we listened to the heavy footsteps treading across the deck. They were not those of the sea captain; we had all quickly learnt the telltale pattern and rhythm of his steps that warned us of the fast-approaching cruelty. The metallic scraping of the locks on the door being opened made my heart jump. I thought with each 'clunk' we were perhaps one step closer to being free from this damp, dark ship.

When the doors first opened, the bright light that poured into the room was blinding. The hot sun beating down, warming my skin, felt almost as comforting as it did at home. Before my eyes could adjust, I felt the cooling breeze hit my face as we approached the upper deck, blinking through the bright haze to take in my surroundings. I had no idea where we were, but it was not home and -although I had never been- I had a terrible feeling this was not Europe either.

There was another ship, like the one we had travelled in from home but larger, anchored slightly further down the shore. I could see hundreds of people on the deck and others queueing to get on. As I was led closer to the ship, I could see with more clarity what was taking place. I realised the people boarding the ship were chained, some desperately trying to pull themselves free. There were men watching over them, forcing people forward and dragging those who refused. Screams and cries coming from the ship became louder as I got closer, as did the looks of apparent terror on the faces of those forced up the gangplank. The blood drained from my face as the realisation set in; whatever was taking place aboard this ship was clearly more gruesome and horrific than anything I had endured aboard the Dutch sea captain's schooner.

After weeks of having little food and water, my body refused to listen to me. I tried to resist being led any further, but my weak legs were barely able to hold up my body, much less resist the strength of the two men either side of me. My throat was so dry that all I could muster through my chapped, bleeding lips, were raspy whispers of protest that seemed to fall on deaf ears.

Once aboard the ship, I saw my servants put in chains; I never saw them again. Two men took me to another part of the vessel with dozens of terrified children. We were all stripped of our clothes and taken down into the hold of the ship. The men overseeing us spoke quietly among themselves. I recognised the language - English. I had been taught English from a young age at the palace, but I could not quite make out what they were saying at such a low volume.

I was left standing there, exposed and confused. I tried speaking to one of the men using the English I had learnt, but he barely acknowledged my existence and pushed me into a wall. I winced as the fragments of the wooden walls pierced my exposed skin. It was clear that I was not going to be told where we were going or what was to become of me.

The only light emitted came from the oil lamps held by the overseers, which I used to guide me. I chose a corner that was the least occupied, to escape the screams and cries of younger children. I tried to make conversation with some of those around me but soon realised there was a language barrier as we were all from many different countries in Africa. I huddled in that corner, mulling over the events that had occurred since my departure from the palace. I tried desperately to understand what had happened the day that the power to decide my fate had so carelessly switched hands.

Chapter 2.

Jamaica

The voyage was unbearable. The smell of urine and faeces was so pungent it burnt our eyes and the back of our throats, and with little food and water, death became a regular occurrence, and the cries of younger children became less and less each day. We remained in that dark, damp space until the ship anchored at its destination many weeks, maybe months, later.

I heard voices yelling that we had arrived at Port Maria in Jamaica. By that time, I had lost sight of reality; I was dying. I no longer questioned what we had done to deserve this; it didn't matter. I welcomed death.

But when the doors opened and the warm breeze passed through and diluted the stench within, I was suddenly jolted; I was alive. I'll never forget the eerie silence as we were unceremoniously marched off the gangplank, sick, weak and naked. Most of the men and women who had been locked in other parts of the ship were still in chains.

Once off the ship, we were promptly scrubbed clean until our skin was raw, a strangely satisfying feeling after the months at sea we had spent, unable to wash, in unsanitary conditions.

Thick palm oil was rubbed into our skin until it gleamed under the harsh sun, making our wounds and sores almost unnoticeable. We were given rags to wear. The rough material did nothing to shield us from the burning sun, which only felt hotter with the thick layer of oil.

The older-looking children like me and the younger ones were then separated from the adults and led towards an enclosure. The overseer leading the way opened the gate and ushered us in like livestock. I realised the enclosure we were put into was an animal pen, but our bodies and minds were so exhausted by the trauma of the voyage, that few had the energy or strength to object.

A while later, several men unlocked the gate and let themselves in. They inspected all of us individually, forcing our mouths to open wide so they could look at our teeth. When they finished, two other men came into the pen, bringing us food. I had not eaten in the past two days, and so I scoffed the food down. We were giving a dark liquid to drink which was distributed out of a bucket. I looked around and saw that the others who had dared drink it, were coughing and spitting it out, something that seemed to anger the man. When he came to me, I closed my mouth, not wanting to drink it out of fear.

"Drink," he said. He was so close to my face that I could feel his breath on my forehead. The disgust and anger that danced in his eyes paralysed me. He snarled and muttered to himself as he picked up the cup and forced the liquid into my mouth. I am not sure what it was, but it burned as it slid down my throat, making me gasp and splutter.

"Wasting good rum on you animals," he cursed. "Lunch is over. Get ready for the scramble," he told us as he locked the pen behind him, that same evil shining in his eyes. 'Scramble?' I thought to myself. I had no idea what that meant.

Soon, people began crowding around the pens. Their casual chatter overlapped, getting louder and louder. More people joined until it became a constant, blaring sound, so persistent, it drowned out my thoughts. They were looking at us the way starving people look at food, almost desperate. I knew those looking at us did not see us as people but more like cattle.

Suddenly, a gunshot pierced the air. I was amazed anything could be heard over that sound, but it was clear that it was possible, as immediately after that shot was fired, people poured into the enclosure. Fear set in as I could hear my heart beating and feel my stomach drop. I saw some of the children scramble to hide behind each other; their high-pitched screams sent shivers down my spine as they were forced apart with such brutal force. I was swept away in the process; it was such a blur I could barely make out in my head what had happened. One moment I was standing in a group, and seconds later, I was being grabbed and pulled in a different direction, before being tied to the back of a wagon along with several others also taken from the enclosure. The sheer scale of what had happened to us was a concept that was hard to stomach.

We continued our journey, barefoot, walking behind the wagon to a mysterious unknown destination.

After what seemed like hours of walking, my feet had become as numb as my mind. We walked past acres of land where sugar cane was being grown. There were men women and children in the fields, cutting down the stems and hauling them onto wagons while overseers on horses rode around them. Although I could see what was happening, the severity of it just did not register in my mind. We finally stopped at a grand house, where we were made to stand in a straight line. I was exhausted from the walk in the midday heat and had a headache so mind-splitting that it mirrored the feeling of someone having cracked my skull with a rock. But after the ramification I received for something as little as not wanting to drink, I dared not complain.

Soon after, a gentleman emerged from the house. He was clearly of a higher class than the overseers; I could tell by the way he dressed. He paused a couple of feet away from where we were lined up. "Today's purchases?" the gentleman enquired to the overseer, raising a brow.

"Yes, sir," he replied. "Straight from Port Maria - fresh batch. Good hard-workers, as promised." The gentleman looked us over briefly as he paused.

"Very well, son, put them to work," he said dismissively as he began to turn around back towards the house.

"But, sir," it seemed to have escaped from my lips before I could stop it. I froze. From what I had seen, protests were met with nothing but cruelty and violence. The gentleman's head snapped back in my direction as his gaze zeroed in on me. He walked over to me; I fought the urge to close my eyes as I braced myself for what I assumed was going to be severe punishment.

"What was that, boy?" he asked me. I was stunned for a second.

For the first time since leaving the sea captain's schooner, my voice was heard.

"I... uh, see," I stuttered, trying to find my words. How ironic, that the first time someone was listening to me, my words were failing me.

"Speak up, boy!" he barked.

"It's just that, erm... I think there has been a mistake, sir. I'm Prince Yohannes and...," my words trailed off when I saw a sly smirk forming on his face. He seemed almost amused by what I was staying.

"Take this one to the house. His name is John, now," he said. "Get him cleaned up", he commanded before turning around and going back into the house. I wiped my clammy hands on the rags I was wearing as I tried to calm the rapid beating of my heart.

I was led in silence to the back of the house, where I was promptly cleaned up and given cleaner clothes to wear, which were far more comfortable than the rags I had to wear previously. I was then taken and left by the door to the kitchen. I stood there, looking in at an older woman standing over a stove; she was peering into a pot. There was a tender nature about the woman.

The gentle lines that formed around her eyes were somewhat comforting, a feeling I had not felt in many months. I stood there, hovering, not knowing if I should go in and interrupt her. She must have noticed I was standing in the entrance, and suddenly, I heard her say,

"Come over here, boy", without even turning around. Slightly embarrassed that I had been caught lurking, I made my way over to where she was standing.

"You're the boy from Africa," she stated in a matter of fact way.

"Yes, ma'am, but I'm supposed to be in Europe," I replied. She paused briefly to look up at me, before scoffing and turning her attention to the pot.

"Now, I don't know where you learnt to speak English...."

"In the palace, ma'am. Back home I'm a Prince, you see...." She raised her hand in a shushing motion.

"As I said, I do not know, and I do not care, you see, you are no Prince here; you're not even a human being in this place.

The best thing to do is keep your mouth shut and your head down. That's if you want to survive."

My eyes widened at the blunt way she was talking to me.

"Now, if you are smart, and you seem to be, then you will remember that and keep those stories of your past life to yourself, because you aren't ever going back. You do not need to forget them; hang on to them all you like. Nobody can take them from you. But don't you share them with anybody, you hear me?" she warned. "You must understand, they bring a lot of people from Africa; many of them die fighting, others are tortured into submission, the rest of us find ways of living," she finished. Her words felt like a thousand knives had pierced my heart, because I had believed that, one day, I would be returning home when they realised I was a prince. Now if I want to live, I must never speak about my life in Africa.

Over time, I became the master's private slave, jumping to his every whim. As the years passed, my memories of Abyssinia started to fade. As they did, so did my sense of identity. I was no longer Prince Yohannes, but John. That was my existence until Brinny arrived at the plantation as a kitchen slave. The moment I laid eyes on her, I felt my heart skip a beat that made me feel alive once again.

Chapter 3.

Brinny's Story, Jamaica

My start in life was darker than most. My father had perished in a vat of molasses some months before I was born. As I drew my first breath on the sugar plantation in Westmoreland parish, my dear mother took her last. Perhaps it was a kinder fate for her not to be around.

Young mothers struggled terribly after childbirth because their babies were immediately   taken from them and sent to be reared by elderly slaves, so the young mothers could slave in the fields, under the blazing sun, whilst battling with their maternal instincts and trying to stay alive. Looking back, saying 'babies raised by elderly slaves' is a stretch at best. We were bred like cattle and, as soon as we could walk, our food was put into pig troughs. Half-starved, we hungrily scrambled to eat the food while our slave masters looked on, calling us little savages and making us believe we were animals instead of human beings.

Those of us who survived the age of four had to earn our keep. We were put to work in the field; our little hands were well suited for pulling weeds. The women working on the plantation took it upon themselves to physically reprimand us in a bid to stop the overseers from doing so, as this was often fatal for children. The quicker we learnt not to object, resist, or talk back, the less frequently we were punished. I quickly learned that the easiest way to survive was to obey and not heard.

I was sold at the age of eight and taken to a new plantation in Montego Bay. I was so pleased when taken into the plantation house to work. Even though I was just a child, I knew it was a much easier life than working in the field under the blazing sun. I soon learnt how ruthless my new slave master was. Floggings were a daily occurrence for me and the other two young houseboys for nothing more than standing in the wrong place. Our skin was left raw and bleeding with no aid administered.

I was fearful of life before it had even begun. I prayed that I would never wake up from sleep. By the age of 11, the master and several of the overseers had taken an interest in me. There were no laws against the rape of slaves, not even children. We were property; possessions they could take and do with us as they pleased. And they did. I was glad to be sold again to another plantation-owner in Falmouth, further north up the coastline, before finally being sold to the plantation in St Mary.

I met Yohannes a couple of days after I arrived at the plantation. I was outside hanging washing and there he was, so handsome and elegant. Our eyes met in a fleeting glance across the yard. I quickly learned he was the personal slave to the master. From that moment on, every time I was in his presence, my heart would beat faster.

I felt so shy and nervous that my stomach tied in knots; it was the first time in my life I had experienced such feelings. He seemed to feel it too, as it took him weeks to pluck up the courage to talk to me. I will always remember that night we had our first conversation.

The master was hosting one of his regular evenings for various plantation-owners and their wives. Yohannes served the men while I waited on the women. It was my first time serving guests and I must have looked nervous because Yohannes gave me a gentle smile to let me know I was doing okay. We stood with our backs against the wall as the guests ate dinner. We listened to them talking about their plantations and how best to control their slaves. I glanced at Yohannes; he had a distant look in his eyes. It was clear to me the conversation around the table had affected him; I managed to get his attention and I gave him a gentle smile. He took a deep breath and smiled back.

After dinner, the men retired to the drawing-room. There, they continued talking business and smoking imported cigars while having their glasses topped up regularly with expensive liquor. The women remained in the dining room, having futile conversations, mostly about the shocking number of babies born to young enslaved girls, pretending to be blissfully ignorant of what was happening right under their noses. The babies' lighter skin and looser curls were not fooling anyone, least of all the wives. They simply had the luxury of convincing themselves otherwise.

When the visitors left the plantation that night, John put the master to bed and returned to the kitchen. I was the last one still working, so there was none of the usual chatter and bustling. His simple smile had me utterly bewitched; I was lost in the dark abyss of his eyes. Yohannes spoke to me in hushed whispers. His English was crystal clear which, when paired with his smooth, rich voice, had the hairs on my body standing up. He said he was forbidden to speak to anyone about his life in Abyssinia but was happy to share his memories with me.

He spoke with such pride about his African country and how he had been born a Prince and named Yohannes after his father. He grew up in a beautiful castle surrounded by the love of his people. He even told me about the amazing animals of Africa, the lions, elephants, and giraffes. I tried so hard to imagine such creatures.

It was the first time in my life I had heard of a story that I could believe in; a dream of a place far away from the brutal world I had been born into. Listening to his story brought tears to my eyes. Yohannes reached out and touched my hand, then looking into my eyes, he said the word 'Ewdehalehu'.

I did not understand what it meant but I knew it was meaningful; I could see it in his eyes. I tried my best to compose myself and contain the gasp trying to escape my lips. I felt love for the first time in my life. I never wanted our time together to end as he was my Prince Yohannes, but the time went by so fast. The sun came up, another day was about to begin, and reality quickly set in. He went back to being John, but from that moment, he would forever be my Prince Yohannes; my dream. We had to put our feelings and humanity to one side and resume our place as the master's slaves until we could, once again, steal some precious moments, moments that made us feel so alive in a life where we often wished we were dead.

For several weeks, all we could do was look at each other lovingly. The way we would gently brush our hands together when we would pass each other made my heart skip a beat. The thrill of my secret romance was a driving force that got me through the days.

Then, early one morning, I was outside fetching water to begin the master's breakfast. Yohannes came out and stood next to me, looking nervously at the ground. I was pulling up the pail of water when he quietly said, "The master has permitted me to take a woman". I let go of the rope and the bucket dropped back down into the well, emitting a loud splash that barely even registered in my mind. I was so stunned that I stood there blinking like a fool with no idea of what to say or how to respond.

"Only if you want to," he said. "It's up to you; you can say no if you want to...." He trailed off, the usual confidence in his voice wavering. He ran back into the house. The sad look on his face made my heart ache. I would want nothing more than to be his; to be his because he asked, because I wanted to. It was ironic that the first time I had the ability and power to make a choice over a man's advance was the one time I had no words.

I had to wait all day to see Yohannes again. My nerves ate away at me as I tried to contain my excitement. I saw him in the hall that evening. He walked towards me, looking down at the ground, avoiding my gaze. As we walked past each other, I reached out and took his hand. He stopped dead in his tracks and looked up into my eyes. "Yes," I whispered as I squeezed his hand before breezing off to the dining room, unable to wipe the sly smile off my face.

It was forbidden by law for slaves to marry but we had secret marriage ceremonies anyway, if only to preserve our dignity and respect for each other. The cook acted as a preacher, asking us each, in turn, whether we chose to be with each other, before placing a broomstick on the ground. Yohannes and I stood in front of the broom. He took my hand and placed it on his heart before repeating the same word he had said weeks before: 'Ewdehalehu'. With that, we hopped over the broom and the cook pronounced us husband and wife.

Although it was not a legal marriage, that had no effect on how sacred our union was in my heart. We had no cake, guests or even a ring and had to return to our duties immediately. Nonetheless, it was the happiest day of my life. We had pledged our love and respect to each other, so whether legally binding or not, I was fulfilled.

Later, I asked my new husband Yohannes what 'Ewdehalehu' meant. He turned to me and smiled, pulling me close and letting his forehead rest against mine. We were so close that the tips of our noses touched, and I could feel his warm breath against my cheeks. He looked deep into my eyes before gently saying,

"I love you". While we were rarely physically that close, from that day forwards, our souls were so entwined that, emotionally and spiritually, I felt as if I was that close to my prince all the time.

Chapter 4.

John's birth

We were both grateful to our slave master as we had a small room at the back of the mansion house. We had plenty of food and clean clothes and we only had each other to protect, unlike other slaves on the plantation who were worked to death, half-starved and had no shelter or protection.

I was born into slavery; this was the only life I knew. My survival as a slave with Yohannes by my side was a dream come true, but how quickly life can change. When I told Yohannes he was going to be a father, his reaction was not what I expected. He was devasted and refused to talk to me. It was as if he was blaming me for being a woman and wanting to bring a child into this brutal life. It was the first time since I had met Yohannes that I felt so alone.

In the spring of 1754, I gave birth to our son. There was a magical moment when Yohannes saw our son for the first time; it was one of the most sacred memories I have. I could see Yohannes come alive again when he held our baby, but it lasted only seconds, then he put him down quickly and walked away.

Our slave master called us both to his study. There, he told us that, as a reward for being obedient and trustworthy slaves, he would name our son John. As the master of the plantation, he named all babies. Very rarely was the world-wide tradition of naming a son after a father enforced. He also gave us permission to raise John until he was old enough to work and earn his keep, just so long as he was out of sight. Whilst I felt blessed by the kindness of our slave master, having grown up seeing so many women not being given the chance I was, Yohannes felt the opposite; he was now filled with such remorse.

Although we were in the same position now, it was times like these that reminded me of how different our stories of origin were.

Whilst we were both treated like caged animals, I was born into captivity as a slave and knew nothing else, but Yohannes was born in a palace, a prince surrounded by the love of his people and family. He had been taken from his natural habitat where he thrived and was left with nothing but the memories to reminisce over. I knew every day he spent in ownership chipped away at his very soul. Although he had accepted his fate as a slave, it broke him to know his son was to face the same life sentence. But, with no option, he would have to suffer in silence.

He distanced himself from me and barely looked at our son. I had been through my fair share of pain in this life so I knew my tolerance was higher than most, but this was more pain than even I could stand. I finally confronted him. "How can you not love your son?" I said to him. Bluntly, he answered,

"John belongs to the Master, not us. I cannot love him or protect him from this life. I am not a father and have no right over him. I am no father," he repeated. His voice broke towards the end of his sentence. His head fell into his hands as he pulled at his hair in frustration. I could, in my own body, feel the pain that I saw in his eyes. I knew there was truth in what he was saying.

Whilst, of course, we were John's parents, we had no say in what would become of our son and we were powerless in influencing decisions made about his future. I could not bear to see Yohannes like this, my strong and powerful man reduced to a shell of who he was meant to be. I crouched down to his level and held him close as he laid his head over my heart. For a moment, we sat in silence with him listening to my heartbeat and me to his breathing.

"You are a father, but you must stay strong and teach him how to survive. We must do what we can for as long as we can to keep our precious angel pure in this horrible world," I whispered to him. I could feel the muscles in his back relax as we sat there, and the tension flowed out of his body. Yohannes pulled away from me so he could look me in the eye as he continued,

"Yes, you are right; he is my son and he is a prince. I will teach my son to survive, but not as a slave."

Fear washed over me. It was forbidden for slaves to have any form of education or free-thinking, much less for us to claim royal lineage.

But then, I realised we had nothing to lose; our son's future was bleak anyhow. I knew Yohannes was planning to give our child hope and something that resembled a life. So, whilst I was scared, I had to be brave for him the way he was being for our son.

Yohannes had an education before being taken into slavery and he was intent on passing all his knowledge to our son. To achieve this, he was convinced that John should not mix with other people on the plantation so he would not pick up their broken English, mindset, or bad habits.

At first, I felt hurt. I knew his intention was to protect John, but him saying that he did not want John to be around other slaves as they would have detrimental effects on him made me feel like the definition of who I was would be harmful to my child. I was a Jamaican mother; how could I not be myself around my son? But I trusted my husband and stood back as much as possible, knowing everything he did would perhaps be in our son's best interests.

Every spare moment Yohannes could steal away, he would scurry to our room to be with John. I worried, at first, that it would be harmful for our son to be left alone so much of the time, but he was always so content and would find ways to entertain himself. He was passionate about learning and listened intently to his father's every word. He was in his element when his mind was being pushed to its limit and asked more and more questions. Without paper or pens, Yohannes taught him about letters and numbers, but he also had to explain to John that he should never be seen trying to read or write, especially in the presence of slave masters, and that he was never to speak of his royal ancestry in Africa. Telling this to our precious child felt like we had cursed him to a lifetime of limitations.

Meanwhile, he had to understand it was essential for his survival in this world.

When John was four years old, he had to start earning his keep and began doing chores in the house, mainly in the kitchen. After several months of him working, John was called into the master's office. Fear washed over us, and our hearts sank. Although Yohannes had explained the importance of respect and etiquette to our son, he was still just a child, unaware of the concept of ownership.

But our worry was unnecessary; the master was immediately taken aback by John's eloquence and etiquette. John's love of words amused the master so much that he began encouraging him more with words, quickly progressing onto pictures and books. He became so fond of John that he proudly began showing him off at his social gatherings. His guests would gather around while our young son would articulately recite what the master had taught him earlier that day - usually a passage from the Bible.

Yohannes could not have wished for more, given our circumstances. Our John quickly took his place as the master's favourite and was, therefore, somewhat more protected from the way of life that had been forced upon us all. We suspected one day the master would tire of him; I feared that day more than anything else in life.

Unfortunately for us, that time came sooner than we thought; it began shortly after John turned six.

Chapter 5.

Tacky's rebellion

Easter Sunday, 1760; a day of thanksgiving and blessing for our slave masters, but for slaves, it was just another day in hell.

The master had been celebrating and had just finished dinner. All was well until an overseer galloped into the plantation, bringing with him news about a slave rebellion that had begun in our parish of St Mary's. The master and overseers grabbed guns before mounting their horses and riding out to look for the rebels.

Word quickly spread around the plantation. I soon learnt through the grapevine that a man named Tacky was leading the revolt. Although I had not heard of this man, many field slaves had. I learned that Tacky had been captured in Ghana, where he had been a Fanti chief, by warriors from a neighboring African country. He had arrived in Jamaica some six years earlier, where he was sold to Ballard Beckford and taken to the Frontier estate.

I knew this was a brutal plantation where new slaves who tried to rebel against their captors were tortured into obedience; a process they called 'seasoning'. It was something that so many of us were forced to go through that a whole term was made up to identify this process. After having gone through this himself, Tacky appeared to conform and adapt to the life of slavery. He appeared to have been reformed into a trusted slave, but he was a man who was biding his time. He had spent years watching the barbaric and abusive egos of the ruling classes; men killed on a whim and women raped for sport.

Tacky had learned how to play the system and, that night, he was set on destroying it. I heard that several men and women had joined Tacky, prepared to die if need be for the inhumane crimes committed against them.

It was late into the night when the master and his overseers returned to the plantation. I thought the rebels had been captured and punished, but early the next morning they mounted their horses and left again, this time with more men and extra guns.

For several weeks, they looked for Tacky and his rebels without success. We got word that the insurgents had overpowered British forces and had obtained firearms and ammunition soon after the rebellion had first begun. They set fire to plantations, which were the core of our brutal existence and our enemy's wealth. For several months, they left destruction and death in their wake as they made their way across Jamaica, with more men and women joining the rebels.

The general governor petitioned King George III for extra military power to suppress the slaves, at the same time calling upon the Jamaican Maroons to help capture Tacky and his rebels.

The Maroons were runaway slaves who had signed a treaty some twenty years earlier with the British colonial authorities, whose strategy was to Divide and Conquer. It was agreed that the Maroons should not harbour new runaway slaves; instead, they would help catch them in exchange for their own freedom. This smart strategy caused a split between the Maroons and the rest of the Jamaican population, dividing the country so slaves could not band together and draw on their strength. The leaders of the revolt were soon hunted down by the maroons, who shot Tacky and several hundred rebels.

The British Empire was victorious. The captured rebels were handed over to the authorities who, in the town square, publicly executed most of them. Others were beaten within an inch of their life and their bodies put on display to slowly die and rot under the burning sun. This was done to act as a deterrent and to instill fear. Harsher laws were put in place to strengthen control over slaves, with severe punishments such as whipping, disfigurement or even death inflicted on anyone seen plotting an uprising or accused of collaboration.

Despite this, news of Tacky's rebellion spread across Jamaica, causing more uprisings to take place, although colonists celebrated victory time and time again. The unrest in the country caused many slave owners to flee Jamaica, leaving their overseers to run their plantations, resulting in even more brutality.

Some plantation owners became a little kinder to their slaves, hoping, in return, that they would protect the farms and not rebel. Nonetheless, the destruction of plantations was damaging to the British economy. In a bid to reduce the costly uprisings and to end the nervous tension felt by slave owners, colonist came up with another strategy, this time to quash familiarity amongst slaves.

For the next few years, thousands of men, women, and even children were randomly moved to different plantations. Many were removed entirely from Jamaica and taken to other colonies across the sea.

John was just nine years old when the master began to avoid him. It started off as him just seeming anxious when John was around, and then he completely stopped talking to him, making him work out in the stables. It was clear to Yohannes and I that our young son was no longer a novelty; the master's shiny new toy had worn dull. The interest in John's rich vocabulary and abstract ideas, which the master had once found endearing and even encouraged, was no more. My boy had gone from being the master's greatest amusement to his greatest threat, or at least the master had begun to realise that, one day, he could be.

We had to prepare our son for his unknown future; we had no choice. Yohannes told him to always hold onto who he really was, to be proud of himself and to keep sacred in his heart that he was, and would always be, an Abyssinian Prince.

The master continued to battle with his insecurities until one morning, Yohannes was told to prepare the horse and carriage, as he was going out and would be taking John with him. He had never done this before. I could feel my chest tighten as John walked towards the carriage. My stomach churned, twisting itself so tight it almost made me keel over, as my vision blurred from the tears that were brimming in my eyes. I fought them back as well as I could, so as not to alarm John. My heart hammered in my chest, the dull thuds echoing in my head, drowning out all other noise till everything else sounded distorted as if my head were being held underwater. It felt like I was dying. Knowing what I knew my son could be facing, I would have welcomed the sweet escape death would have given me. Yohannes intercepted John moments before he reached the carriage. He quickly pulled him tightly against his body, holding his head against his shoulder before whispering "Ewdehalehu" in his ear. Almost immediately, he released him and held him at arms-length, aware of the prying eyes of the overseers.

Yohannes cleared his throat and stood up straight, patting John on his back before John turned around and got into the carriage. Soon after, the master came out and joined John. Almost immediately, they set off into the unknown. Every fibre of my being was telling me to chase after him, to get my son and face the repercussions later.

"I, too, want to protect our boy," Yohannes said to me, knowing exactly what I was feeling, not moving his gaze from the horizon beyond which John had just disappeared. We knew we would never see him again; all we could do was stand by and watch him disappear from our lives forever.

Chapter 6.

Polgreen's Story, Barbados

I had travelled to Jamaica to visit the blue mountains on the eastern side of the island; it is where the most splendid coffee beans are grown high in the mountains. I was hoping to arrange export of this coffee to Barbados, where I owned a decent hotel that catered for gentlemen, sailors and sometimes even royalty. I was ready and prepared for the intense ten-hour trek over steep terrain to reach the summit and had eight experienced guides to lead the way. Halfway into our journey, I became exhausted and desperately wanted to turn back. Thankfully, my guides were full of support and encouragement, telling me not to give up but to simply focus on putting one foot in front of the other, that every step I took was a step closer.

When we finally reached the summit, I was overwhelmed. I sat down and took in the breathtaking views across Jamaica. Despite not getting the business deal I had hoped, I never felt that the struggle of the journey was in vain. Not only had this trail allowed me to discover the hidden beauty of an island so close to the one that had become my home, but it also taught me things about myself I would never otherwise have remembered.

As humans, very few of us know how strong we truly are. It is something we are not forced to tap into until being strong is the only choice we have. Sitting on the top of the mountain, breathing in the sweet, warm air that had travelled thousands of miles across the Caribbean Sea, I felt at one with my surroundings.

The only thing that could be heard from all the way up there was the birdsong that filtered through the high canopy of trees, different tunes and pitches coming together from an array of different tropical birds to form a perfect harmony. It was peaceful to be away from the constant drone that seemed to always follow wherever people went, if only in the background. Our descent was just as breathtaking.

I stayed at a small inn while I waited for a ship to take me back to Barbados. After several days, I became restless, so I travelled into the town centre where, unbeknown to me, a slave auction was taking place. I stood back and watched as people were bought and sold like cattle. I had myself purchased several slaves previously, so I was familiar with the process.

As I looked on, I noticed an exquisite boy around nine or ten years old. I watched as a refined gentleman stepped away from the boy, who was steered forward and made to stand on a slave block. I was taken aback at how elegant this young boy looked. As the bidding began, he glanced over at the man who was selling him; the fear and confusion were evident in the boy's eyes, while the gentleman seemed completely unaffected and turned away from him.

Without thinking, I raised my hand, and after the count of three, the hammer came down – "SOLD". In the blink of an eye, the boy's fate was in my hands. Whilst, by law, he was now my property, to me, he was my responsibility. Although I may appear to be an active partaker in the slave trade, my intentions were more honourable. My aim was not to keep people like possessions, but to best equip them with skills I hoped in future would pave the way for them securing a position that would allow them to live their lives as people, as opposed to property.

After the auction, I asked the young boy I had just purchased what his name was and how old he was. He bowed.

"My name is John, master. I'm ten years old."

"Sir or Mr Polgreen is quite sufficient," I replied.

"Thank you, Mr Polgreen," he replied. As we began to walk towards the port, I told him we would be leaving Jamaica and travelling to Barbados as soon as we could. I asked him how he felt about leaving this island. He replied, "I cannot tell you how I feel, sir; I am but a slave".

I was somewhat taken aback by his reply, yet, at the same time, so impressed by his pronunciation of English. It was later that same evening that we were able to board a ship heading for Barbados. During the journey, I asked him how he had learned to speak such good English. He told me that his father had taught him, something I thought highly unlikely, although he looked sincere. I did not believe that his father, a man taken from Africa and sold into slavery, possessed the knowledge or the ability to be able to pass the said education on to his son.

Having lived in the West Indies for quite some time now, I had, time and time again, been exposed to the horrendous treatment slaves had to endure. I knew that the circumstances this boy would have been born into were simply not designed to facilitate any sort of development. The decks were stacked against him.

When we arrived in Barbados, the ship anchored in Bridgetown port. From there, we had to climb onto a barge called a lighter that transferred us from the sea onto the island. Though all these experiences must have been new and therefore quite daunting to a young boy, John remained composed. He certainly was like no other child I had ever met.

Once we arrived at the hotel, I introduced John to Malacky, he managed the hotel for me. His family had come from Ireland fifty years earlier, after they signed an agreement with the British Empire to become indentured servants, providing seven years of labour for food and shelter. In return, at the end of the contract, they received payment in the form of land or capital. Malacky was a man deeply saddened by the burden African slaves had to carry. He had worked as a gentleman's butler before he came to the hotel and was happy to pass on his skills.

John was eager to learn and quickly settled in. He was very well-received by visitors, not only for his elegant manner but also his engaging conversation.

Many gentlemen recognised that John was an exceptional young man and offered to buy him from me, even promising to give him a good position as a personal slave in their homes. I knew none of them would be worthy of such an admirable young man, especially here in Barbados. I had no intention of selling John to anyone in these slave islands of the West Indies.

Over the next couple of years, I watched John grow in confidence and engage fondly with Rachel. She was a young girl who frequented my hotel, usually when trying to escape the sexual advances and beatings from her father, William Lauder. He was a Scottish schoolteacher who had left any morals he had in the sewer after he had written and published attacks on the widely renowned republican and English poet, John Milton. But before anyone could respond to his verbal attacks, he fled the country for the warmer climate of the West Indies.

Rachel's mother was a young enslaved girl, born native to Barbados, who was unfortunate enough to have been bought by William merely for sexual purposes. He demanded complete control of her body and mind. When their daughter, Rachel, was born, she hoped the abuse would ease. But it did not, and when he began to make sexual advances on his young daughter, all she could do to protect her was tell her to run and hide.

Over time, Rachel developed her own ability to dodge her father. She was an intelligent girl and had a savvy streak that was born out of self-preservation. She learned everything about the running of the hotel and would often say that one day, she would manage it. I was extremely fond of her, but I could do nothing to help her as she was a slave who belonged to her father.

Thankfully, John was in a slightly different position, where the power to decide what was to become of him was held by myself and my intentions were more honourable than most. It was a constant inner emotional turmoil, knowing how much power I held over those young people in my care. I had no place being allowed to make those decisions; only the individual themselves should be able to. However, every time I saw one of those young men or women blossom into people in their own right, I knew that it was worth the philosophical conflict and I became more and more encouraged to help as many more young people as I could.

John was different from most of the others as he had been educated from a young age, a luxury that very few had. His elegance and refined etiquette meant that his potential would only have been capped at my hotel. No, bigger plans had to be put in place for John. Selfishly, I wished to keep John here in Barbados with me but keeping him trapped here on this island he had already outgrown would defy the purpose of me having taken him on.

Over the years, I had developed business relationships with several others in the hotel business, mainly in London. They, too, catered to the upper classes and aristocracy but simply on a larger scale, being in the busy and bustling capital city. The opportunities and situations John would experience in such an environment were much more to his calibre than anything I could offer him in Barbados. Staying true to my intentions, I reached out to my peers in London to enquire whether they would be willing to take John on.

They were all intrigued by the way I had described John, and several were keen to meet him, I suspected out of disbelief at how highly I had spoken of him. They had never heard of a young boy who possessed the level of eloquence I described and were even more taken aback when they learned about the circumstances in which I had met John. With the meetings set up, arrangements for our travels were soon underway. From

Carlisle Bay in Barbados, we boarded a slave ship that was on the final leg of the Atlantic route, returning home to England. Now, instead of human cargo, the vessel was loaded with sugar, rum, ginger and other luxury commodities, the valuable profits, of the slave trade.

We arrived in London in the late summer of 1767, where a childhood friend of mine had graciously offered to accommodate John and I. While the purpose of this trip was to find a suitable position for John, staying with my friends was a personal pleasure. Having left London to fully commit to my hotel in Barbados so long ago, I had lost touch with many of my friends.

Living in the West Indies meant that I had missed out on years and years of European news, from the political unrest born out of fear of losing the American colonies due to the new increase in taxes, to the building tension between Russia and Poland. I made a point to educate myself on what had occurred in my absence and kept up to date on any developments by reading the newspaper every morning.

Several days after our arrival in London, I remember reading the morning paper while eating breakfast, something that had become a routine of mine. I came across an article about the rising conflict in the Americas. The Townshend Act was on course to be implemented, an act which would increase taxes to protect from potential future French incursions. When similar acts had been enforced two years prior, riots broke out across several states, so this delicate matter was a frequent topic of conversation amongst my peers.

Despite the severity of what was going on in the Americas, what caught my eye was that a royal entourage had arrived in England with eight-year-old Prince Radziwill of the confederacy of Biala in Poland. He was in exile until the conflict had been resolved, to protect the rightful heir.

The royal family of Radziwill was one of the wealthiest dynasties in 15th and 16th-century Europe, with estates in Poland, Lithuania, and Belarus. I got to work immediately and started contacting the various people in my network, with whom I had connections, who could get me in contact with the young Prince's uncle. I knew from the newspaper article that he oversaw the Prince's care.

It took several weeks for me to arrange a meeting with the Prince's uncle. They were also staying in London, just a carriage ride away. I could not help but feel that the coinciding of the Prince's and our arrival in London was meant to be. I met the uncle and arrangements were made. I thought, 'What better place for John's talents to be capitalised upon than amongst royalty?'

I remembered back to the day I had purchased John at a slave auction, when he told me his father had been responsible for setting the foundation of his early learning. This I believed to be highly unlikely, as slaves born into slavery were denied education and those born free in Africa and sold into slavery were not educated in the ways of the western world, therefore they had neither the power nor even the knowledge to teach their children.

I was wrong; an Abyssinian father with much wisdom and compassion did lay the foundation for his son to be able to shine in a world that would deny him basic human rights because of the colour of his skin.

With John's eloquence and mannerisms already matching those of European aristocracy, I knew he was well-equipped to join the royal entourage.

It saddened me to have to part ways with him, but he deserved to move on to bigger and better things, things that I simply could not facilitate.

With that, and a heavy heart, I let him move on to pastures new.

Chapter 7.

John's Story, England

The carriage arrived to take us to meet the royal Radziwill entourage, where I would take up a new position as a personal valet to the young Polish prince. James travelled with me to make the initial introduction, as he had been the one who had organised this new position for me. I must have looked nervous sitting there, because soon after the carriage set off, James looked over at me and said, "Don't worry, John, you'll do great. Your life will be one filled with wonder and adventure." I simply smiled back at him.

Truth be told, I was not scared. The fluttering in my stomach came from a place of excitement, not fear. Since meeting James, I had been able to explore parts of my personality that I never knew were there before, which made my confidence grow immensely. It is hard to have any self-belief when you yourself do not know who you are. James had done a lot for me, so no matter how twisted it was that he had that authority over me, I would eternally be grateful to him for all he had done.

"Thank you, sir," I said after a few moments of silence had elapsed. James looked up from the book he was reading. Looking at me from over his glasses, he enquired,

"What for?", as if almost confused or taken aback by my comment.

"For caring," I said and shrugged, not sure how else to describe it. There was a kind twinkle that shone in his eyes, the same look that had immediately put me at ease when I first met him. He truly had equipped me with the skills and attributes I needed to succeed, and I knew I was going to be okay.

The look lingered for a second before he returned his attention to the book. I sighed in contentment and leaned back against the comfortable chair and looked out the window, taking in the scenery and impatiently waiting for our arrival.

Once we arrived at our destination, introductions were quickly made. I was shown to a room where I was introduced to the gentleman who was currently in charge of the prince's care. Whilst James was discussing matters and formalities with his uncle, the gentleman explained what my role would entail. He discussed the prince's routine with me and told me about all the different activities I would take part in alongside the prince. I was to be shown how to dress, wash and prepare his clothes and I had to be by his side most of the time, even as he attended his various lessons and excursions.

Several hours later, James emerged with the uncle and the prince. I was taken aback by how young the prince was. With his extensive entourage, schedule and all the detailed instructions I had been given, I was expecting him to be much older. He looked only several years younger than me and had a boyish nature about him, complete with a cheeky glint in his eyes and wild tousled hair. Unsure of how he would react to me, I fixed my posture, standing up straight. I waited for the three of them to get closer before bowing to him. As I stood up, I looked him straight in his eyes, pausing cautiously to see whether he would initiate conversation. He blinked at me before looking up at the gentlemen I had been waiting with and spoke to him in a language I did not recognise but could only assume was Polish.

Their exchange only lasted a minute or two, after which the boy turned to me and grinned. With the prince speaking little English and English the only language I spoke, there was a language barrier between us. He started heading towards the door at the far end of the grand room we were in, before turning back and making a beckoning motion with his hand.

Perplexed, I instinctively looked at James, who offered me a small nod. I quickly started heading to the door. The prince waited for me to reach where he was standing before walking with me, leading the way to where we were going through big, heavy wooden doors that were opened by the men standing on either side.

As we continued down the hallway, I looked back, catching a glimpse of James watching me walk away. Our eyes locked from across the space. The last thing I saw before the doors clanged shut was him waving farewell, our final goodbye.

"Umm...," the prince muttered to himself, touching his index finger to his mouth, clearly deep in thought as his brow furrowed. "Me and you," he started slowly, pointing first at himself and then me, "we learn now," he told me. And just like that, I became a pillar in the prince's life. From that moment on, I remained by his side as both he and I had the novel experience of absorbing the British culture.

We stayed in England for the next 18 months, which was enough time for me to get a pretty good grasp on the Polish language. With the language barrier being eliminated, the prince and I quickly became close. I suppose that was inevitable with the amount of time I spent by his side.

He was only five years my junior, which I think is why we were able to build the type of relationship we did. He had no prejudice or pre-existing perceptions of me the way many other European-looking people had back on the islands.

From my initial arrival, the Polish people treated me with the utmost and equal respect. For the most part, so did many of the British people.

The variety of ways of life in London was something I was not prepared for. When the prince and I would be in the carriage travelling around London, I remember how intently I watched as we passed different areas of the city; the perfectly manicured gardens in Highgate that stood outside luxurious mansions; a show of great wealth and grandeur. Then, not too far away, the slum areas of the city, extreme poverty, rows of tattered houses with shattered glass windows and a putrid smell that seemed to linger in the air. Many unkempt children were roaming the streets some begging others stealing.

The stark comparison between two areas of a city that were so close together boggled my mind. I had expected to see prosperity and wealth, but I never imagined that I would see such extreme poverty here in England.

When it was time for us to move on from England, travel arrangements had to be made for the next part of our trip. We were to go to a country called France. The journey was by far the most comfortable one I had been on, as I was travelling alongside the prince. It was strange; some of the people we met along the way, such as the man directing the carriage, called me sir. Being treated as an equal was a strangely comforting feeling that I still had to get used to.

Strangely, the gentleman who helped me unload the luggage from the carriage when we reached the port, referred to me as Mr Bridgetower. I believed my name was John Polgreen since meeting James, so I was confused as to where that name had come from. When I was, soon after, handed my travel documents to present as we boarded the ship that was to take us to the northern coast of France, I looked closely at the details that had been written down.

There was, indeed, an error; instead of being John Polgreen from Bridgetown, Barbados, I was listed as John Polgreen Bridgetower from Barbados. They had likely not heard that Bridgetown was the capital city of Barbados, which I had travelled from, and as such, assumed I had two surnames, something I had seen quite frequently in England.

I considered correcting them and having the error rectified on the documents, but the more my mind pondered the situation and I repeated the name out loud to myself, the more I liked the sound of it. So, for the first time, I decided and made a choice. I would now be Mr John Polgreen Bridgetower.

Chapter 8.

France

My life in France was very similar to the way it was in London; I still spent my days with the prince, responsible for his washing, dressing and his personal hygiene and accompanying him to his lessons; the culture of the country was simply different.

We stayed in the magnificent palace of Versailles, where instead of English lessons and being taught British history, the prince was now being taught French history, language, and music. The elegance and musical sound of their language worked in perfect harmony with the graceful notes emitted by the various classical instruments. I relished the opportunity to learn a new language and eagerly listened to the tutors as they gave the prince lessons.

By being so submerged in the French language, I soon picked it up and began using my ever-growing vocabulary to have small conversations with the other staff in the palace until the words fell from my lips as naturally as my name. It soon became apparent I not only had a talent for words but an ear for musical notes as well.

While I learnt to play the piano and cello, the classical instrument that spoke to me most was the violin. There was something about the way the device emitted the smoothest notes, that seemed to pour out from it like melted butter when the strings were teasingly caressed by the bow.

I will always remember the first time that euphoric wave of appreciation for the art of music washed over me _ the first time I heard Chevalier de St-Georges play. I had the pleasure of becoming strongly associated with him when he started giving the young prince private music lessons.

Chevalier de St-Georges was a 24-year-old public figure in France; a violinist, composer, athlete and one of France's greatest swordsmen, he was admired and respected by all. His father was a French aristocrat who was a part of the inner circle of King Louis XV.

His mother, however, was a young enslaved woman whom his father had purchased in the French West colony of Guadeloupe. Although Chevalier had an excellent education and lived the life of a courtier, he was not entitled to his legal title or even marriage under French law because of his African heritage. Thus, while on the surface, individuals like Chevalier could take part in polite society, it was very much at their discretion. There was an underlying inkling of something darker lurking beneath their apparent acceptance.

While in Paris, the King had betrothed his 15-year-old grandson, Louis-Auguste, to a 14-year-old Austrian Princess,

Marie Antoinette. By the side of the young Prince Radziwill, I was fortunate enough to attend the royal wedding, which took place on the 16th of May 1770. It was a spectacular event, enhanced by Chevalier de St-Georges' personally attributed contribution to the music.

I stood back and watched him play the violin. I felt immense pride as I looked around at princes and princesses, lords and ladies in the grand hall and saw the delight on their faces as he played; I was mesmerized by him.

In one of the last conversations I had with him before we left Paris, he urged me to understand and recognised my fortune, stressing how the young Prince Radziwill was my protection from the treacherous world beyond, and the foundation I needed to succeed. He said it was crucial that I continued to learn. He believed my fluency in language and growing knowledge was fundamental in helping to overturn the growing beliefs that Africans had no intellect, compassion or human feeling. I understood what he was saying and promised to never stop learning. I wanted to follow in his footsteps and was so happy when he said he had seen a younger version of himself in me. I was so proud to say he was a friend of mine.

The royal entourage set off on the journey. Our next destination was Italy as we were still unable to return to Poland because the battle with Russia continued to rage.

In Italy, we stayed with Carlo Galeazzo Busca Arconati Visconti at the Del Caretta villa in Tremezzo on Lake Como. While there, I absorbed not only the Italian culture and language but also the beautiful scenery. The only body of water I had ever seen was the sea, a powerful force of nature that stretched as far as the eye could see. But here in Tremezzo, we had a lake instead, calm and serene, surrounded by huge mountains with soft peaks that seemed to jut out of the surface of the earth randomly.

I stayed close to Prince Radziwill and encouraged him with his music lessons, all the while learning alongside him.

Although other musicians were all extremely talented, none of the professors of music could muster anything that spoke to me the way Chevalier de St-Georges' work did, perhaps because I had so much admiration for him.

Chapter 9.

Poland

As the conflict between Russia and Poland had finally stabilised, we were able to return home to Biala as it was now safe for the prince to do so. The year was 1772.

My integration into the Polish culture was seamless and natural. Having spent the last five years with the Polish entourage, my grasp on the language was nothing short of perfect. With the prince being so young when he had to leave Poland for his protection, extra care and measures had been taken to try and keep his environment consistent.

So, whilst travelling with the entourage, I incorporated as much of the Polish culture as possible; from natural aspects such as the manner in which they interacted, to more refined details that could be controlled, such as ensuring the books the young prince read and the music he listened to were Polish. This allowed me to learn to understand their culture before even visiting the country, as I was so submerged in the culture daily.

I became so confident and comfortable in speaking the language that I was often commissioned as a translator for the aristocracy and upper classes in Poland.

My linguistic ability, indeed, was the most substantial factor that led me to become well-known and respected amongst the royal families of Europe, and it was surreal.

If someone had told me that I would be travelling the world alongside a prince when I was back in Barbados, I would have thought they were criminally insane. Logically, there was no way for me ever to be presented with the opportunities I was given, yet here I was and what a way I had come.

As is the custom in many royal courts in Europe, princes married princesses to keep bloodlines exclusive to those who had managed to claw their way up to the upper echelons of society. Young Prince Radziwill and German Princess Sophie Friederike of Thurn und Taxis had been betrothed for many years, although both still just children.

When she turned sixteen, the beautiful Princess Sophie arrived in Poland with her royal entourage for their wedding. It felt as if preparations for their wedding started immediately after their arrival. I had been to one wedding before that, and that was the celebration of the marriage of Prince Louis-Auguste and Marie-Antoinette.

Still, I had never imagined that they were such important events and came with deeply embedded traditions, specific to each culture. Princes and princess from all over Europe attended.

I stood by the side of Prince Radziwill and greeted the guests as they entered the grand hall, then introduced them to the royal couple.

Soon after the royal wedding, I grew increasingly closer to Maria Ann Schmidt. She was the personal servant to Princess Sophie and had travelled with her from Germany. In a way, I suppose I always knew I was going to fall in love with her. With me acting as the Prince Radziwill's right hand and she as Princess Sophie's, we spent so much time together that it was almost inevitable.

I have never wished I could stop time as much as I did in those moments we had together where it was just the two of us. Initially, I was unsure of her feelings, but our friendship started developing. Innocent acts, like a look that lingered a little longer than before, a flirtatious smile and carefree laughter, became more and more frequent. I always knew my feelings for her were real and genuine, but even during my time in France, I had never been faced with an inter-racial couple that was openly together.

I had never even heard it discussed, whether it was a taboo subject, simply not allowed or was just coincidentally something I had not experienced and was unknown to me, so I was scared to share my feelings with Maria. I feared the potential backlash. As time went by, I continued to watch her.

At times, she was so close I could reach out and run my fingers through her hair, but was so controlled by fear that the idea made my stomach drop.

Then I realised that what I should fear was not the potential repercussions, but the potential to have missed my chance at happiness due to my own insecurities. It became more apparent, over time, not only that Maria knew and accepted my feelings for her, but that she shared in them too.

As our love for each other grew, we became increasingly committed to each other, to the point that I even got baptised just in case one day I could perhaps marry her. The empowerment of my love not being limited by factors that were crippling in other countries spurred me on to make a decision about my name for the second time; I was baptised John Polgreen Freiderike Bridgetower, paying homage to my new ties to the Germanic culture.

We were young when we met, and therefore, inexperienced. I had clearly seen more of the world in the first 18 years of my life than most people did in their whole lifetime, but by no means did I think that meant I had experienced life; really experienced life.

I had yet to feel love. Not the kind of love that one feels for their parents, the kind that warms your heart so much it almost burns, the love that keeps you awake at night, terrified at the mere thought of losing it. I wanted to see more of the world, travel across more oceans, feel more masters of their instrument touch my soul with their music. The more I got to know Maria, the more I realised that she was the woman I was destined to embark on this adventure with. I wanted to live, not just be alive.

The opportunity I had been given to leave the West Indies was one that was so rare, I felt an immense amount of pressure to make the best of it. There was this onus on me to do right by everyone who had helped me, from my father, to Polgreen to the Radziwills, and to live fully for all of those who could not, and would likely never get the opportunity to.

Before long, we went to the prince and princess to tell them of our courtship. With the prince and I having such a close relationship, it had been difficult for me to keep this to myself for so long. I think a part of me had not shared it with him earlier because I was concerned about what his reaction would be. He was more than someone I worked for; I truly cared for him and, as such, valued his opinion of me. To my relief, not only were they both tolerant of our romance, they encouraged it, even expressing their desire to be present at our wedding.

We had a small but magical ceremony with the prince, princess, and local gentry present, who all blessed our union. We were finally and eternally bound together in holy matrimony.

On 11th October 1778, Maria gave birth to our first son, who we named George Polgreen Bridgetower, after Chevalier de St-Georges. He was someone that I so much admired, I had kept in touch with him over the years by letter. It felt right that my firstborn be given the name of the man I was able to look up to with such pride; I hoped, one day, my son would follow in his footsteps.

But my son, George, was a very sickly, sensitive, and vague child. He slept a great deal, which made his mother and I worry that his life would be short. So, we quickly had him baptised with the names Hieronymus Hyppolitus de Augustus in the same ceremony where Prince Radziwill and Princess Sophie were appointed as his godparents.

To our relief, as time passed, George became physically stronger. He always remained an expressionless child and made no eye contact with us, being almost cold and distant. Two years later, our second son, Freiderike, was born. He was the opposite of his older brother; his laugh and squeals filled the hallways from the moment he took his first breath.

My boys were truly the opposites of each other; Freiderike would choose to interact with everyone, while George's eyes would glaze over when being spoken too. Maria and I despaired over his future, which looked bleak. There seemed to be no life in him, no spark in his eyes or fire in his belly. He simply existed.

The massive shift in my mindset that took place after I became a father took me by surprise. I knew that being a parent was a life-changing experience, but I was not prepared for it to change as many parts of my life as it did. When I looked at my two children, memories of my childhood came flooding back.

I remembered how my mother and father had told me if I wanted to survive in this life, I would have to look up to the very people who persecuted us without conviction or question. Now, as a parent myself, naturally, I feared for both my son's futures and promised them I would not let their life pass in slavery.

During the day to day duties of raising my sons, I often thought about Chevalier de St-Georges. I began to understand, with more clarity, the situation he was in, thus the more it outraged me. No matter how highly respected he was in France due to his exceptional talents, he was only really accepted by those of the highest class to a certain point. He was welcomed at the parties, allowed to part take in conversations about his contributions to the country's vast culture and commissioned to play the most exclusive events. Yet, if he ever wanted to share his marvellous life with someone, he was limited in who he could share that with.

Perhaps it took me finding my beautiful wife and having children to realise how important that is. I never knew what was missing from my life, not really realising that I was feeling unfulfilled until that gap in my life was so perfectly filled by Maria.

Knowing what I knew now, the idea that someone so celebrated publicly, would be denied such a basic and natural source of happiness that we, as human beings had, seemed cruel. I could no longer say and do nothing, sitting idly by as this world continued to operate in a manner that would inevitable limit not only my sons but all people who shared in their ethnicity and breeding.

I would not have my sons grow up in a world where they were held in lower regard than their European peers. Their heritage should be something they were proud of, a source of empowerment, not a life sentence. My parents had done a miraculous job of shielding me from the horrors that most children who entered the world in the same circumstances as myself were forced to suffer.

It was my duty to carry forth those values and instil them into my own children too. But to truly protect them, I had to open their eyes to the darkness, not hide them from it. How were my boys supposed to learn to protect themselves from issues they did not even know existed? No, that was no way forward. Ignorance, misinformation, and poor communication were the roots of the problem, so it surely would not be its undoing.

From that point forward, I became extremely demanding towards both boys, teaching them etiquette, speaking to them in Polish, French, English, German and Italian. We assumed that Freiderike would be the child who grasped the languages quicker. From a young age, he had been more outgoing, speaking to Maria in German for extended periods of time and using the little he knew of the other languages confidently when talking to me.

Incredibly, it was George who grasped the different tones of the language, although still very quiet and withdrawn. When introducing the piano, cello and violin to my son, George excelled even though he was just five years old. He was able to read music before he could read literature. George played the instruments repetitively, especially the violin, needing no encouragement from me. Maria and I recognised that George, although indifferent to other children, was a truly gifted child.

When he began performing, there was no shyness or awkwardness. The only time he seemed to be at peace was when he would stand in front of his audience and play as if he were the only person hearing it. People were amazed, taken aback by his talent. I was an extremely proud father. The rewarding sensation that would fill my body when I would see people recognising my son's gift was intoxicating, making me feel almost giddy.

Knowing his talents were being celebrated and not overlooked or dismissed, as I had initially feared, gave me hope for this world. His talent breathed a new purpose into me. I intended to show my remarkable son off to the world.

My opportunity came when Nikolaus II, Prince Esterhazy, came to visit the Radziwill Palace. He was part of one of the wealthiest, most influential families in the Austro-Hungarian empire. He was a patron to the musical arts; his Palace boasted an opera house and he employed the renowned Franz Joseph Haydn.

I seized the opportunity to introduce George to Prince Nikolaus by having him play the violin as the prince entered the palace. This was to the great delight of Prince Nikolaus, who was impressed, not only by George's playing but by my expertise in the differing cultures and languages. He offered me employment as a doorman at his Palace.

I knew this was an opportunity for George to become familiarised with an orchestra most importantly an orchestra conducted by the renowned Joseph Hayden, this would be a key stepping-stone in my son's professional development. Although I loved Poland, and was grateful to Prince Radziwill and Princess Sophie, after eighteen years, I now had to put my family's welfare first. This was a fantastic opportunity for

George and Freiderike, so Maria and I decided to move our family to Austria.

Chapter 10.

Europe

In Austria, I quickly settled into my role at the beautiful Esterhazy palace. I was thrilled when showing visitors, the exquisite architecture, and the stunning concert halls where George played the violin, cello and piano with an orchestra. Princes, princesses, and various gentry were amazed by his talent.

His mother and I would watch in wonder as audiences gave George standing ovations, hoping the recognition of his gift by the masses would give him the confidence in his personal life that would match that in his musical career. Yet, at the end of every performance, he would bow in the gentlemanly way I had taught him, collect his belongings, and step out of the limelight, without any type of reaction to the great applause.

We were very happy in Austria; everything seemed to be going to plan. George was growing and developing faster in the music world than I had anticipated, establishing himself at the age of six through connections he made by playing with some of the most widely renowned musicians and composers.

I knew then that I had to use the full extent of my own personal network of connections to further his dominance of the arts. It was time for our family to move on yet again, to the next stage of our adventure. After Austria, there was an interim period of just over a year where our family remained united. When considering what would be the best move for George and Freiderike's careers, Maria and I decided on Germany, the epicentre of musical development at the time.

Whilst in Germany, I became acquainted with Ernst Schick, a great virtuoso violinist. He took such interest in George that they performed in many concerts together, included one for Joseph II who was the Holy Roman Emperor ruler of Habsburg Lands and the brother of the new French princess, Marie Antoinette.

However, not all our time spent in Germany was as pleasant. Maria and I were lucky enough to be blessed with another child, a boy we named Johannes after my father. Tragedy struck when our baby died suddenly as an infant, with seemingly no apparent cause or reason. The boys were too young to really understand what had occurred, but the loss weighed heavy on Maria and me.

The only way I seemed to be able to cope was to throw myself into managing George's career. Several months later, I decided to take George to France to show his incredible talent to a broader audience. Freiderike was becoming a great cellist, but George was such an exceptionally talented child, I had to let the world know about him. Maria was troubled but she understood my reasons; she, too, believed in George's gift. She said he needed to be seen by the wider world for his beautiful being, talent and intellect.

I left, leaving Maria and my younger son, Freiderike, in Germany, something which seemed not to bother George of course. I was relieved at how well he was adapting - no parent wants to see their child suffering, especially due to a decision they had made. Any other nine-year-old child would have been distressed by the sudden loss of their mother and brother, but, as always, he showed little emotion.

In France, we stayed at the home of Chevalier de St-Georges. He was still the toast of France, but he had now become involved in the anti-slavery movement, calling for the abolition of the slave trade. This movement had been founded two years earlier in England by Granville Sharp.

Chevalier de St-Georges was helping to set up a similar campaign in France called:

'The society of the friend of the Blacks.'

I was once again taken back by St-Georges; he was clearly a great man, but I had my young son and I had to give him my full attention. He needed to be seen for his amazing talent.

I was shocked to see that France was in such turmoil because of inequalities between the rich and poor. The streets of Paris had become extremely intimidating, especially for the wealthy. Nonetheless, George continued performing and even performed with Chevalier de St-Georges; for me, that was the greatest show on earth. But the major debut performance for my son in France took place at the Concert Spiritual Hall on 13th April 1789, where he performed a violin concerto by the Italian composer, Giovanni Giornovichi.

I was looking around at the enchanted audiences and the distinguished guests the way I normally did, riding the high that my parental pride had triggered, before noticing the United States minister to France his name was Thomas Jefferson. He was accompanied by his daughter and her 14-year-old personal slave, Sally Hemings. I watched him looking at her like a sexual predator; she looked so uncomfortable.

The sight of that beautiful young girl, who I knew had no legal capacity to say no, sickened me to the point that I could no longer hear George play. The ferocity of my own personal thought drowned out anything else as memories of Rachel in Barbados fleeing the sexual interference from her father came flooding back to me. My heart broke for her all those years ago when she told me she was nothing but property, and one could sexually abuse one's own property.

The guilt was overwhelming. When I had left the West Indies, I was so focused on what I was leaving behind, what I was escaping, that I completely suppressed all thoughts of who I was leaving behind. I had a duty now, to act as the voice for all of those who had lost their own. After the performance, the great hall was filled with applause and wonderment. For the first time, I felt disconnected, preoccupied with thoughts about matters bigger than myself.

I often read the papers to see what the reaction to George's ever-growing presence in Europe was. After reading the reviews of his most recent performance, I realised that his presence in the upper levels of society was making a difference; I knew I had to keep pushing.

The papers stated that;

"His talent is one of the best replies one can give to philosophers who wish to deprive people of his nation and his colour of the opportunity to distinguish themselves in the arts." One audience member reported:

"I have just watched the debut performance of a young prodigy, George Augustus Polgreen Bridgetower. His playing is perfect, with a good clear tone, spirit, pathos and good taste."

Although I was delighted at news reports about George - it was the highest-profile praise he had received to date - I was still unable to silence the thought of deeper, darker matters in my head. At the time when we were there, France had other pressing issues to worry about because the French revolution was now looming. Thousands of French nationals, mainly from the upper classes, were leaving France at an alarming rate. It was becoming unsafe for us to remain in France, but my newfound mission and purpose was too important to be abandoned.

Determined to keep pushing, I soon realised that we would have to relocate to England so I could keep pushing my cause without impeding George's career.

Chapter 11.

London

George took London by storm. He was greeted with great applause, especially by HRH the Prince of Wales. The upper classes in London spoke of a miraculous young violinist, making HRH eager to listen to George play privately.

The Prince of Wales was an extraordinarily vain and extravagant man. He spent vast amounts of money gambling, drinking and entertaining nobility at Carlton House in London. Even when political opponents questioned the waste of public funds and the social injustice of his lavish lifestyle, he shrugged them off.

Two years passed; he accrued so much debt that the House of Commons had little choice but to increase his income and pay off his debt. After that, he selfishly commissioned the building of the first part of the luxurious Brighton Pavilion, which was to house his personal orchestra with the best musicians of the time.

George and I were invited to Charlton House as he was planning a private concert for his father, King George III, who had sunk into a deep depression after having lost the American colonies.

The exclusive performance was held at the Queen's Lodge in Windsor Castle and was recorded for the occasion:

"An adventurer by the name Bridgetower, a black, came to Windsor with the view of introducing his son, a most possessing lad of ten or twelve years old, an excellent violin player. He was commanded by their Majesties to perform at the Lodge [the Queen's Lodge], where he played a concerto of Viotti's and a quartet of Haydn's whose pupil he called himself. Both the father and son pleased greatly, the son noted for his talent and modest bearing, the father for his fascinating manner, elegance, expertness in all languages, beauty of a person, and taste in dress."

King George III and Queen Charlotte were delighted by George's playing.

After that performance at Windsor Castle, George and I were travelling around England when one British newspaper reported:

"A young negro, named George Bridgetower has made his entré into the world as a musician and promises to be one of the first players in Europe. His natural genius was first cultivated by the celebrated Haydn; he speaks many languages".

News reporters were eager to talk to us, so I took the opportunity to tell them about my own father being an Abyssinian Prince and being sold into slavery by the Dutch sea captain. I candidly told them about how he was supposed to take my father to Europe for an education, but instead, stole his wealth and sold him as a slave to a plantation owner in the British colony of Jamaica. After that report went out, I was dubbed the African Prince.

While George was thrilling audiences with his musical talent on the violin and selling out venues across England, I became involved with the anti-slavery movement. I had become one of a dozen intellectual African men living in London who had joined to form *'The sons of Africa'.* They campaigned relentlessly for the abolition of slavery. Through this group, I had become acquainted with two authors; one was Olaudah Equiano, whose autobiography detailed the brutal treatment of slavery. His book was published in England and quickly became a best-seller. It was used by abolitionists to bring awareness of the horrors of the Atlantic slave trade to the people of Europe. Another friend was author Ottobah Cugoano; his book publicly demanded the total abolition of the slave trade and freeing of slaves.

Both men travelled around England together, selling their books, hoping to educate the public on the injustice and brutality of slavery by the European colonies.

To contribute to the cause, I began using my position amongst the ruling classes to promote the injustice of slavery and the concept of human rights that had begun in France.

I brought attention to issues that sickened me to the stomach such as the brutality and the rapes inflicted on slaves without any law to protect them, I spoke of the lies that were written in newspapers, books and taught in classrooms, all claiming that African slaves had no human feelings compassion and lacked intellect. Some people were upset and shocked by my claims.

I had my work cut out; these lies were widespread and were continuing to do so at an alarming rate. It was both frustrating and simply infuriating how many people believed what they were being told, idly swallowing the labels being forced upon people from the African continent.

Many people applauded me, but others with more of a financial interest in the slave trade looked on with such disgust, selfishly worried that my honesty would affect their businesses. They wanted me silenced, so they brought it to the attention of HRH the Prince of Wales who, incredibly, took my son from me and had me removed as his guardian.

Even though I argued that, my son, George was not a citizen of England and should be returned to me immediately, HRH claimed that he was taking George for his own protection. Claiming that my supposed severity ultimately forced George to run away from home and seek shelter with the Prince of

Wales in Charlton House. The Prince claimed he was protecting George from me, and therefore would not be returning him to his family. In an official note he said:

"After years of hearing about the talents of George Bridgetower, I have finally taken him into my patronage. He will live in my Royal Pavilion in Brighton, teaching me music theory and playing in my "personal" band. This will mean taking the boy away from his parents, but I am sure he will understand the benefits of this; after all, who would turn down the fame and fortune of being the Prince Regent's favourite? I will pay the father £25.00 and take care of his son."

Signed, the Prince Regent.

I was consumed by grief, fearing for George's wellbeing and that his African heritage would be the subject of shame for him in England.

Although George was a great violinist with impeccable manners, he was vulnerable and unsophisticated in the ways he showed emotions. He had no interest in vanity or praise in any of its forms. These were all things that I understood about George and therefore could help him with. These people did not care for George the way I did; they would not love or protect him the way I did.

On the 14th August 1789, a press report by the Chester Chronicle stated that: "The musical world is likely to be enriched by the greatest pandemonium ever heard… A youth of 10 years old, a pupil of the immortal Haydn, who performs the most difficult pieces on the violin and goes through all the mazes of sound with wonderful spirt execution and delicacy. His name is Bridgetower, a stable plant of African growth. Thus, do we find that genius does not solely belong to the tincture of the skin. He is now at Brighthelmstone, under the patronage of the Prince of Wales."

To show my son how proud I was of my African heritage, I began to dress in exotic Abyssinian attire at my son's concerts and, as I sat amongst the ruling classes, the violation of my human rights consumed me as I watched my son from a distance. I became more vocal for the abolition of slavery and demanding for human rights.

The press was up in arms and began to place notices in the papers now discrediting me. They accused me of being nothing more than a drunk and a fornicator, claiming I gambled and was most comfortable when spending my son's money after having sold him to the Prince of Wales.

A series of newspaper articles were published, every one more insulting and damaging than the last.

In January 1790, one newspaper reported that I was,

"obnoxious to the genteel English public after having appeared at a function of the Prince of Wales, advocating the abolition of slavery".

Another one in March 1790 stated that,

"The African Prince, as he is styled, appeared as an advocate for the abolition of slavery, his character something of a mungo stamp".

Then, in April 1790,

"He styles himself an African Prince, upon what authority, we will not pretend to say. He is, at present, in a state of insanity".

It seemed the only way the ruling classes could hide their awkwardness on the sensitivity of the subject of slavery was to dismiss it instantly. I was ordered to leave England and to go back to my wife and son in Germany, leaving my son, George, who would have to remain within the confines of the Brighton Pavilion to be a member of the Prince of Wales' personal orchestra. I did not know where I was going to go. I had lost my son, my firstborn, my purpose. I could not go back to Germany without my son.

The life I had become accustomed to was no longer. I was enraged that the prince had stolen my son and I used that emotion to fuel my bravery. When I was removed from England, I was taken to a port and put on a ship to France. From there, I was instructed to continue my travels to Germany back to my wife and family, but plans changed after my arrival.

When I reached France, the French revolution was underway, with the 'Declaration of the Rights of Man and Citizens' spurring it on. I was ready to fight for equal rights and freedom for all my compatriots taken from Africa and sold into slavery.

Chapter 12.

Haiti

From France, I travelled to the French colony of Saint Domingue, also known as Haïti, in the West Indies. I arrived in the winter of 1791, joining Toussaint L'Ouverture. My education and knowledge led to me being appointed Lieutenant-General mentor to Toussaint L'Ouverture, he had begun forming an army with military precision, made up of hundreds of men and women united, ready to fight for their freedom. After three years of fierce fighting, France officially outlawed slavery in all its colonies. However, the battle in Saint Domingue continued as the British and Spanish fought to take over the French colonies, but they too were defeated by L'Ouverture's trained soldiers.

Saint Domingue found some freedom until Napoleon Bonaparte seized political power in France in 1799. Napoleon created a constitution that gave French landowners more power, but he was soon under pressure from them to reinstate slavery in the French colonies.

Napoleon responded to their pleas, once again plunging Saint Domingue into war. This time, Napoleon sent some twenty thousand troops called 'The elite of the French army' with specific instructions; to regain control and reinstate slavery in Saint Domingue.

He ordered that no blacks holding rank above that of a captain were to remain on the island. Toussaint L'Ouverture was captured and taken to France in irons, where he was imprisoned in a fortress then left to starve to death in a freezing cell. However, as I was a British subject, I was returned to England and imprisoned in Bridewell Asylum. I later learnt that the battle continued in Saint Domingue as new leaders took over from those expelled. France struggled to take control, eventually leaving the island. Saint Domingue was victorious as France proclaimed the independence of its former colony.

However, this rebellion had sent a sensation of nervousness throughout the world as it posed an immortal threat to all European slave colonies. They feared that uprisings such as this one could spread to other territories.

A secret decree was signed in 1802 which expelled all officers of colour from the army.

Chapter 13.

England

After having been in the asylum for what felt like years, I was walking outside in the grounds of the asylum when I saw a young man. I don't know why, I just knew it was my son, Freiderike. I stopped briefly and just stared at him, frozen in disbelief.

"I'm so happy to see you, my son," I said as I composed myself. After 14 years of not seeing my son, I could not stop myself from embracing him.

"We have a lot to catch up on, Father," he said as I held him close. I nodded in agreement before leading him to my room, a sparse space with a bed, table, and meagre cooking facilities. I received a parcel of food every week and had the luxury of being able to prepare my meals myself.

It seemed that I had a better standard of wellbeing in Bridewell Asylum than most others, something I suspected was down to the Prince of Wales. While my wrongful incarceration by no means made me fortunate, the manner and conditions that I was subjected to were far better than those of the other patients around me. I spent a lot of time teaching some of the inmates how to read.

Freiderike and I sat down. I no longer just wanted my son to understand the reasons for my seemingly cold actions; I needed it.

Drawing in a deep, slow breath, I began:

"I'm sure you have many questions, my boy, and I will do my best to answer them all. But firstly, I need you to understand something. If you walk away from this conversation today with one piece of information, let it be this. I love my family; I never wanted to desert you, your siblings, or your mother. But I could no longer see my children growing up in a world that refused to recognise your talents and abilities because of the colour of your skin, especially as you have all grown up to be such incredible people. I could not have asked for anything more from any of you. I am so unimaginably proud, and I know your mother is too." Freiderike quickly reassured me:

"We know, Father. We did not know much about where you were or what you were doing, but you loving us? That was the one thing we never questioned." I was relieved to hear this. For the first time in years, I felt almost at peace.

"So, what happened? We all had our questions and theories, but none ever seemed to quite add up," Freiderike prompted. "When I arrived in England with your brother George, I was quickly reminded that I was a man who was so undeserving of any respect or fundamental human rights, reduced to nothing but the colour of skin. I had escaped slavery when I left England and travelled to Poland with Prince Radziwill.

"Being given to the prince was the last time I was seen or treated as stock. I was no longer a slave, but a person. I saw things and met people that before I only thought existed in fairy tales and children's stories. I became a part of what my brothers and sisters dared only to dream. I was able to forget about the horrors I had witnessed in the West Indies.

"When the Prince of Wales took your brother, I felt like I had lost purpose. I had failed as a father and as a husband. He was my son, and I had brought him to a place where I did not possess the ability or power to take him back home to you and your mother, where he belonged. It was one of the times I felt most powerless in my life. I could no longer close my eyes. I realised that no matter what we achieved; we would never be truly worthy.

"The secret decree that was signed in 1802 did not just expel Africans from military ranks, but from every profession which opened the possibility for them to be seen in the public eye or known internationally. Africans that were already successful in Europe would no longer be acknowledged.

"Such as it was with my dear friend, Chevalier de St-Georges, who died a couple of years prior. He was once the toast of France. Now, much of his work has been deliberately destroyed, stolen, and locked away as if he never existed. I fear that you and your brother will meet the same fate, being written out of history books and forgotten, leaving no legacy for future generations.

"I realise I could have perhaps done more for the abolition if I had kept a level head and stayed in Europe, instead of going to Saint Domingue to fight for our freedom there. Now I fear the secret decree will hold us back for hundreds of years." Freiderike sat looking at me, trying to process and understand what he had just heard.

"It is so good to see you, my father," he then said, snapping out of the trance-like state. We embraced. "How are they treating you here?" he continued. "I'm okay; I've survived worse and I have my own room," I said dismissively, not wanting to dwell on myself any longer.

"I will see extra food and newspapers are brought to you often," Freiderike promised. I looked up at him and clutched his hand, smiling proudly at my son who had grown into such a caring and considerate man. Maria had done a fantastic job of raising him. "Thank you."

"So, tell me, what have I missed?" I enquired, eager to hear how everyone was doing. "After having not seeing George for 14 years, it took Mother and I completely by surprise when he showed up at our house in Germany he is, of course, as reserved as ever, He told us that HRH the Prince of Wales had suddenly given him leave. Coincidentally it was the same time you were returned to England and incarcerated for the rest of your life, George brought the news that HRH had decided to support Mother with an annual payments from the royal staff account while you remain in confinement.

"Mother was curious as to why the HRH the prince of wales wanted to support her. she insisted that it was out of a guilty conscience for wrongfully imprisoning you and taking George from you, they disagreed George saying you were happy to leave him, she was terribly upset, and promised never to touched any of the money. Worry not; she knew that if there was anything you could have done to remain by George's side you would have," he told me.

"He's doing well, though, very well for himself. He became extremely well-known across Europe; he even became acquainted with Ludwig van Beethoven, who presented George with a tuning fork and named the sonata after him. They even played together in the Augarten-Halle in Vienna." He continued; "But you know what George is like. He can come across as...," Freiderike paused, trying to find the words.

"I know," I said, reaching out and placing my hand on his arm in understanding. George was a brilliant but troubled mind; explaining something as complicated as his mind was no easy feat. "They fell out; it was a big scandal. George did not speak about it much; as always, he was not one for conversation. But I heard that Beethoven told him he was in love with a woman, but she was not in love with him, something that was troubling him. When he introduced the two, George's arrogant and dismissive attitude toward her caused her to tell Beethoven that he had insulted her.

"Blinded by his adoration for her, Beethoven ended his new friendship with George and ended up renaming the sonata after Rudolph Kreutzer. Even that did not seem to faze him," he finished. It was a lot to process, and honestly, what bothered me most was that George thought I would do such a thing to him. I had always known he was not the warmest, most emotionally forward person but I had hoped that he had at least felt safe and secure in the knowledge that I loved him and would never leave him.

"What about you, my son?" I asked him.

"I am making a good living as a musician, playing the violoncello. I was also giving English lessons at home in Germany. I'm doing very well," he told me. We continued to catch up on all the lost time, with Freiderike telling me about growing up in Germany with Maria and me sharing stories of what I had seen on my travels. The hours flew by, feeling like minutes.

Before I had even realised how much time had elapsed, the time for his departure had come. We said our farewells and he promised to come and visit again when he could. I felt relieved, knowing everyone was doing well. Especially my sweet Maria. This conversation gave me the much-needed closure I was not aware I was lacking.

Several months later, I was outside in the grounds of the asylum when a newspaper reporter came in and started talking to me. Though at first, I was disinterested, yet after a moment of pondering, I thought it was an excellent opportunity for him to tell my story.

There was hope of being able to continue my work from confinement. The year was 1805 but I was soon crushed when the report came out stating:

"The pretender, John Polgreen Bridgetower otherwise Lieutenant-General Mentor, lately serving under Toussaint L'Ouverture, otherwise the Black Prince.

This person speaks fluently English, French, German, Italian and Polish languages, a man of "colour", a fine figure about 40 years of age, he is in confinement."

They had nothing good to say about me or why I was in detention, wanting only to further tarnish my name, but there it was.

On 25th March 1807, Freiderike came to visit me again, as promised, bringing with him good news. Firstly, British parliament had outlawed the Atlantic slave trade. It meant no more people would be taken from Africa and transported across the Atlantic Ocean to be enslaved in British colonies.

I had waited for this day, but I never thought I would live to see it. It was a blissfully victorious moment and a significant step forward for the abolition movement, even though slavery was to continue in the British colonies. At least now, there were more and more people who hoped and dreamed of a world where a person was seen for who they were, not just their race. In pursuit of that dream, the abolitionists would continue with their efforts until there would be freedom and equality for all men.

The second part of the good news was that he had met a girl by the name of Eliza Guy, and they were planning to marry in the new year. Freiderike had always been so sweet and caring, I knew he would be a great husband and, in due time, a great father too. Maria was planning on coming to England for the wedding and she was coming to visit me. I was so happy I could not wait to see her.

Then I received news, in the form of a letter, from my son, Freiderike. It contained the sad news that my dear wife, Maria, had died in Buisson in Germany on the 8th of September 1807. Guilt overwhelmed me when I thought about all the promises I had made to her about what kind of life we would lead together, painting a picturesque image, before sacrificing our life together, when I was no longer able to close my eyes to the inhumane treatment the European powers had inflicted upon African slaves. I chose my direction, I had to go and fight against the injustice of slavery it was the right thing for me to do. I had loved Maria from the moment I met her and, even now, the husk of a man my incarceration had reduced me to, but my love for her never wavered.

Freiderike continued writing to me and making at least one visit a year to see me. He and Eliza went on to get married on the 6th of January 1808, and several years later they had two children, a daughter they named Catherine, followed by a son they named Frederick, spelt as the English version of Freiderike. He was born in 1812; my first grandson.

I looked forward to his letters; they were the one link I had to the outside world and my family, of which I tragically had lost another member. I received a letter from Eliza, my daughter-in-law, telling me that my loving son, Freiderike, had died of a short-term illness on the 18th of August, 1813.

I was numb, having lost so much over my lifetime. I began to get used to the emptiness that loss left behind, feeling more at home in the darkness than in the light.

My heart broke for Eliza; she would now be left to raise two small children by herself. Desperate to try to ensure she was supported, I wrote to George asking him to look out for her, but George never answered any of my letters.

However, Eliza, my daughter-in-law, wrote often telling me not to worry about her and my grandchildren as they were okay and that the children were getting a good education thanks to George. She told me my young grandson, Fredrick, was also a promising violinist. I was so happy to hear that.

Then she went on to tell me something that made my heart skip a beat. As I read her letter, my eyes misted. She felt that I should know that from the day I was brought back to England, it was George who had looked out for my wellbeing; my accommodation, my food parcels, clothes, and papers, even money, were all down to my son, George.

I don't know why I thought it was HRH the Prince of Wales who was looking out for my wellbeing. I should have known it was George, but I thought he despised me and believed I had left him, or even worse, sold him to the Prince of Wales, but I guess I never really understood my son like I thought I did. I knew he struggled with closeness, but I realised George loved; he just showed it in a different way to other people.

George is in his thirties now and although I don't think he is lonely, I do believe that life without love isn't life, so I pray he might find some love and happiness with someone the way I did with his mother.

Chapter 14.

Mary's Story, England

Mary, darling", I heard my mothers' shrill voice sound through the house, waking me from my sleep. I kept my eyes firmly shut, hoping I would drift off back to sleep and my mother would find someone else to torment.

As I heard her featherlight footsteps skipping down the hall, closer and closer to my room, I knew that my peaceful morning was now going to be anything but. She swept through the door, strutting straight to the windows where she whipped the curtains open. Pale yellow sunlight glared through the windows. I could feel it warm against my face before I groaned and turned around, shielding my body from the warming light with my bedcovers.

"Get up, darling, it's a beautiful day out. So much to be done," she said in her sickly-sweet sing-song voice as she moved closer to the end of my bed. I pretended not to hear, burying my face deeper in the pillows. Suddenly, she ripped the covers off my body, letting the cool air hit my skin, sending a shiver through me.

I sat up in bed, shooting her a cold look as she walked back to the door, satisfied that her mission of disturbing me had turned out a success. She paused briefly in the doorway, putting her hand on the frame before looking back at me. "It really isn't lady-like to wallow in bed all day; you ought to be up early, bright-eyed and bushy-tailed. How on earth will you find a husband?" she snipped before swiftly pulling the door shut behind her and walking off down the hall.

It came as no surprise to me that, even when I was sleeping, I was somehow the human embodiment of disappointment; I always had been to her since my father died. My father, Edward Leake, was a successful businessman through his ownership of various properties and his involvement in the cotton industry.

He died when I was just an infant, leaving my mother to care for me, my brother Edward and half-sister Clara, not that she ever really did. Both Edward and I inherited equal shares of our father's extremely wealthy estate, while Clara, who was biologically not our father's daughter, was bequeathed £5000.

My siblings had always been proper enough to please my mother; Edward was the head of the house; Clara was the picture of sophistication and I was the one with whom they all wondered where they had gone wrong. Clara was the epitome of a high-class lady; softly spoken, in the presence of male company she was extremely shy and would only speak when spoken to. She truly exceeded all expectations of a lady of her standing, as Mother would often say, making no secret of the fact that she wished she could say the same about me.

My brother Edward, like Clara, led his life in a way that aligned with what society expected. He was a pompous gentleman who believed women should know their place, something he and I did not quite see eye to eye on. He was so arrogant and thought he was head of the house. He acted as if everything on this earth belonged to him, like he could lay claim on everything from the tobacco in the Americas to the tea in China. He even altered our long-standing family name, adding the name 'Leach'.

Being the only male heir, he was responsible for the finances and the family business. Edward perfectly fit society's image of what a true gentleman should be.

I, on the other hand, had always been keener on marching to the beat of my own drum, uncomfortable with the limits that society, and mainly my mother, tried to force upon me. She was intent on finding me *'a proper gentleman of a high standing'*.

My appearance seemed to attract several men who would be classed as eligible suitors, but they were all too dull to hold my attention for more than a fleeting moment. I'm sure they were all pleasant enough, but I knew that I was not meant to spend my life with an average, or worse still 'pleasant' man, who passively walked the path that others expected him to travel.

Although emotionally strained, we all had an extremely fortunate upbringing. Growing up in Kensington Square in

London, our home had cooks, maids, cleaners and nannies, the same as all neighbours did. Tutors would come to our house and teach us literature, languages, the arts and such.

As with everything else, when it came to us being raised, it was easier for my mother to employ someone than to bother herself. Since Father passed, she had always been more interested in her newest love interest as opposed to her children. I thought when she remarried Jonathan Hopkinson things would get better, that we would have something at least vaguely resembling a family dynamic again. But instead, she would disappear for months on end, even leaving us to our own devices when we had outgrown our nannies.

Luckily, our Aunt Isabella had a more naturally warm and maternal nature. She had three daughters of her own; Catherine, Claire, and Emma, and she would often include my siblings and I in their family activities. My father had always been good at that, making time for us. Maybe that is why it was so difficult for our mother to spend time with us afterwards, but that was the time we needed each other the most. I remember the summer days I would spend with my siblings and cousins in Hyde Park, squealing excitedly as we ran around, chasing each other. The world truly was a better place when looking at it through rose-tinted glasses.

When it came to family, however, I had to look elsewhere. The place I felt the most at home in my house was downstairs in the kitchen. I adored our housekeeper, Elizabeth Profit, and I like to think she was fond of me too.

When my father died, he had also bequeathed £30 to her in his will. And although Elizabeth had her own young daughter, Alice, she always had time to give me a little bit of extra care and attention. When Elizabeth passed, I was so sad, then her daughter Alice came to work at our house. She was just the friend I needed at that time, so whenever things would get too much for me, I'd go down and see her, and today was just one of those days. Although we both came from hugely different walks of life, we had essentially been raised together by the same woman in our early years; she felt much more like a sister to me than Clara.

I went down to the kitchen to find Alice; she was there tinkering about, singing to herself softly as she did. I jumped up on the kitchen counter, perching myself on the edge so that my legs hung off the side. "So, what's happened now?" she enquired, raising a brow. I had to contain my laugh as I looked at her standing there, one hand on her hip and the other grasping a folded tea towel; she was a spitting image of her mother. I groaned in frustration, not even sure where to start, but that was all Alice needed to know. She knew simply by just looking at me that I was struggling. If that did not prove that Alice was the family I had never had, I do not know what would.

She did not say a word as she set about boiling a pot of water for tea before pulling up a chair at the table and patting the place in front of her. I walked over and sat across from her before letting my fears, doubts and frustrations pour from my lips. I took my hat off. "I cut my long hair," I said to her. All she said was, "Okay, what happened?"

I continued. It had been a particularly gruelling evening where we were entertaining people in our Kensington home, with, as always, Edward and Clara being the golden children. There were only so many hours of my mother pursing her lips at my appearance, rolling her eyes at what I contributed to the conversation and sighing in disappointment that I could take. Sick and tired of being told how to walk, eat, talk, socialise and so much more, I was at my wit's end. Why must the world take all decisions away from women as if we were these delicate, mindless beings? So, that evening, I cut my hair. Where there were once golden locks of loose waves, there was now a honey-coloured curtain of hair that barely brushed my shoulders. But I could not bring myself to throw my hair away, feeling weirdly connected to it, as if it represented me before I ventured off to create my own destiny. I saved it in a heart-shaped box with a key, keeping it tucked away behind old clothes and trinkets in my wardrobe, hoping it would be a source of strength to me one day. It was a small and seemingly meaningless act, but it was important to me. I had to do what I could to feel empowered and in control.

I must have gone on for hours, but not once did Alice's attention waver from me. She listened intently, offering a gently arm-squeeze or disapproving raise of the brow where appropriate. After I was done and we had finished our idle chit chat, I shot her a cheeky, knowing look and left the kitchen.

Chapter 15.

Meeting George

That evening, I was somehow trapped into going to one of my mother's suffocating stuffy and stuck-up soirees, this time in the form of a concert. She had been talking about her grand 1815 Christmas party for weeks now, raving about the music that would be performed that night.

Of course, an incredibly talented musician was not enough for her; oh, no. It had to be someone so spectacular that they had gained the attention of the aristocracy and royalty. When she learnt of who was playing, she became insistent that we must all be there to hear him play; it was something individuals in her circles were discussing.

If there was one thing my mother hated more than anything, it was being late to the newest craze. She prided herself in always being at the forefront of any new up-and-coming trend. Knowing it would be an evening spent with the same limited circle of people from the upper classes she mingled with, I almost wanted to come up with a lie to get out of it. I had no intention of dealing with the repercussions of not going, so I decided to suffer the several hours over having to endure the alternative, that is, days of her nagging.

My heart dropped when we arrived at the venue - it was exactly what I had dreaded; plastic people leading seemingly picture-perfect lives, lives that would have been perfect if they were not a complete figment of their imaginations. Imagine my surprise when, about an hour later, the rest of the audience and I were confronted with the evening's performer.

A Mr George Bridgetower, 38 years old, he was of German and African heritage. I was transfixed, not able to move my gaze from his physique. I did not mean to be rude and stare. I simply could not help myself; I had never seen anyone like him before.

He was tall with an athletic build, broad shoulders, and a tight abdomen. I could tell by the way his body moved beneath his well-fitted shirt. His tight black curls were neatly trimmed, letting his straight nose and full lips take centre stage of his face. His clear skin had a deep richness no other man seemed to possess; there was almost this glow from within.

His facial expressions were the opposite, dark and mysterious. His dark brown eyes were shut tightly as he played the violin; he was clearly a master of his craft. There was almost a sadness that seemed to surround him like a dark cloud. It was by no means aggressive, angry, or annoyed, but almost blank, like there was no emotion there. I was trapped under his spell for the whole duration of the performance, only coming back to reality when the audience's loud applause forced the clouds in my mind to lift.

After the performance, I decided to see what the rest of the audience thought, see what information I could gather about this mystery man. As I milled around aimlessly, casually eavesdropping on conversations as I slowly worked my way across the room, I learned that this man was incredibly admired, with the pretentious upper classes feeling it was an advantage to say they knew him and to have him mix amongst their company.

I was shocked; in my whole 21 years of life, I had never seen this group of people ever work to gain someone's respect or attention. With their place in the highest echelons of society, the roles were normally reversed. It seemed I was not the only one intrigued. I watched as Edward tried to engage in conversation with George, walking over to where George was standing with all eyes on him. I was too far away to hear what Edward was saying but I could see him approach George and place his hand on his shoulders as if they were childhood friends. He said something then that made a gentle laugh ripple through the room, but George barely looked at him.

If there was a single, isolated moment when my curiosity turned to desire, this would be it. I had never seen someone so authentic and true to themselves that they did not bend and break under the pressure of conforming to expectations, saying or doing what one must to be accepted into their elite inner circle. He clearly had no desire for a tedious conversation with him or anyone else. He bowed at Edward in a gentlemanly manner and left, walking past me without even a slight glance. Feeling this thrill I had never felt before course through my veins, it was like I was having an out-of-body experience. I was not in control of my person; my legs were working on their own command, and before I could do anything to stop myself, I found myself slipping away to follow him. He wasted no time making his way straight to the carriage that was waiting for him outside, carrying with him only his violin. He opened the door, got in and closed the door behind him all in one fluid movement. And then he was gone.

I could feel the smile slowly come over my face as I remained in my covert position, tucked away out of sight. I replayed the images of him in my head as I walked back to join the rest of the party. I knew that the feelings that were churning inside me were forbidden, but maybe that is what made them feel all that much better. It was an unspoken rule that a high-class British lady such as me could not be with a man of his heritage. It was something so taboo, so scandalous, that it was not even spoken about. No one ever bluntly said that it was not permitted, it was as if the mere idea of it was so dirty people dared not let those words escape their mouth. But where others saw a rule that was to be followed, I saw a line that was to be crossed. And I was going to cross that line, no matter what it took.

The next day, I made the necessary enquiries to organise private music lessons with him, which were quickly organised for the following week. My mother was visibly taken aback; she had tried for years to get me to pursue a gentler, more ladylike hobby. This may have been the first time she wasn't completely aghast with a decision I was making; she would never give me the satisfaction of telling me she approved, but I could tell by the slight smile she had as she watched me set on my way to George's Highgate home for my first lesson that she was pleased. Despite the fact that her reaction was likely purely positive as she could use this as a status symbol, her daughter being taught by the George Bridgetower, the newfound peace was nice.

I was nervous when I first arrived, waiting by the door for him to come and show me where our lessons would take place. Having heard so much about his talent and abilities, but little about his personal life, I felt like I was going in blind. I had no grasp of his personality, a slightly nerve-wracking experience. When I saw his elegant form breeze down the stairway moments later, he looked as meticulously groomed as I remembered him looking on the evening I first met him. I had previously pondered how much preparation his refined appearance took, but it became clear that was simply the way he conducted himself. He was a strange man, but in all the best ways possible.

During our first lesson, I tried striking up a casual conversation, dropping anecdotes of my own life where I could in the hopes that he would reciprocate. But he never did. He was always polite; he would look at me, avoiding my eyes, and give a small nod, sometimes accompanied by a slight smile to confirm he had heard me and then would return to work. He seemed to give me no reaction, even when I teased him gently, saying,

"You're a good listener, aren't you? You don't talk much". Nothing. It was becoming ever so slightly frustrating. Not to sound spoilt or entitled, but things had always come easy to me, at least, a lot easier than this. I had always had lots of friends and an array of suitors and my father had made sure that my siblings and I would never want for anything before he passed. But with George, he just did not seem to care. Not about my appearance, status, or attempted advances.

If it had been any other man, I think I would have, at that point, refocused my attention, but that seemed impossible with him. He had unlocked parts of me inside that I never knew were there: bravery, vulnerability.

So, I persevered, and over the next few weeks, I scheduled more and more music lessons with increasing frequency. I continued with the small conversations casually scattered across our time. I could not tell if I were making progress and growing closer to him or, simply becoming more and more comfortable around him. Regardless, we were soon spending a significant amount of time together, not only from the lessons but other rendezvous. I managed to convince him to join me for a dinner after a late practice; it was then we passionately made love. I was in love with him, so I was determined to understand his mind. Although he told me about his brother, Freiderike, and his wife, Eliza, and their two children, he said little about his mother and father but I just knew that there was more beneath the surface, more to him than met the eye. He was not simply a quiet, introverted person; there was something deeper there.

It had only been a couple of months since our first encounter when I found out I was pregnant, something that gave me such a thrill it felt like my whole being was made up of electric currents. I knew I had to tell George, but with him still being so distant and disconnected, I was concerned that he may decide he no longer wanted anything to do with me. But I could not hide this from him, so the morning after finding out, I bit the bullet and travelled to his home to tell him. He and I discussed it at length, well, I spoke extensively, and he listened. I used the slight changes in his facial expressions to conclude whether he agreed or disagreed with what I had said.

Together, we decided to get married as soon as possible, and on 6th March 1816, we got married at St. George church in Hanover square. It was an incredibly small ceremony, with only my Aunt Isabella and half-sister Clara present. I knew I had to tell my mother and brother soon, but I wanted to stay in the moment for a little while longer.

A couple of days later, we told my mother and brother that we had gotten married, keeping the news of my pregnancy secret for now. My mother almost fainted with shock, crying out the question: How could her daughter embark on such a union with such a person? Edward's reaction was no better. He ranted about the disgrace I had brought on the family name by marrying a man of African descent, completely disregarding that George was eligible and highly respected. The family name could not have been all that sacred to him, seeing as he changed the name, adding Leach as soon as he got his power-hungry little claws into it. But I did not care what he or anyone thought; I was too full of glee. I was happy; married to a man that made me feel alive and bringing new life into this world. Admittedly, I took some pleasure in my brothers' apparent discomfort when telling him that my husband, of African descent, would now equally be dealing with the family business and all financial transactions alongside him.

George did, however, ensure that his involvement in the family business did not hinder his participation in the world of music. He still had many acquaintances from within the aristocracy who called on him to perform, and as that was the one time I could almost feel his troubled soul rest, I was more than pleased that he continued to share his gift. My family may have been content being stuck in an old-fashioned mindset with dated values, but I, on the other hand, was not. It seemed ludicrous to build a future using ideologies from the past, and I would no longer partake. My happiness would not be limited by the minds of people too small to see past features that were merely skin deep.

In September 1816, I gave birth to a girl. We called her Felicity. It had been six months since our wedding, and of course, there was gossip. Some people even shunned us, not that I cared what they thought. If they formed an opinion about my marriage because of the colour of my husband, it held no merit and, as such, was not something I would lose any sleep over.

My marriage to George was not without complication. It was rare to see him smile or happy. Although I loved him with all my heart and was excited for us to build our family together, most of the time I was not sure if he loved or even liked me. Nonetheless, I was as happy as I had ever been in my life, and it was because of my baby daughter. I loved every moment with her. Even my brother Edward fell in love with his baby niece. Edward never understood George. They had a minimal conversation. Edward often referred to him as a melancholy.

George was very fond of Clara; her soft voice and unassuming ways allowed him to talk about his doubts or troubles within the family and he came to trust her. Initially, I was filled with jealousy when I would see him talking to her or smiling, not the way he smiled at me. This was a special smile that brought warmth to his face and light into his eyes, a real smile, although it seemed to be reserved only for Clara and Felicity.

Naturally, I wanted him to be happy, to have someone to talk to and confide in. But was it so wrong that I wanted that person to be me? I had seen him, persuaded him, fallen for him, and then loved him, but it still was not enough, and I could not understand why. I tried to do all I could to support and be there for him, but it seemed the more I opened, the more he withdrew into himself, which overwhelmed by me.

All at once, I was too much and not enough. Over time, I decided that he needed to have someone he was close to and if that person was Clara, so be it, as I always had been the incomplete version of her. I suppose some things never change.

Chapter 16.

Italy

We decided to relocate our family to Italy in 1819. George grew restless in London, and I had always wanted to travel and see Europe, especially the sunny lands in the south, so we settled on Rome. I hoped that the change in scenery would allow George to relax and let his guard down a little, that maybe going on this adventure together would bring us closer, and we would emerge stronger than ever. All I had ever wanted from this was for him to love me as passionately as I did him.

Months had passed since our arrival and still, he was the same, remaining withdrawn. For several months, I wrote it off as growing pains, convincing myself that once the dust from the shock of such a big life change had settled, he would come out of his shell. But as the months went by, I had to face reality; George simply had no desire to love or be loved. We mixed amongst the upper classes and were friends with an Italian noble, Carlos Busca Visconti, who looked at me the way I had wished George would look at me, so I gave in to my selfish desires.

Carlos was young and handsome, but more importantly, he loved me. I never wanted to have to go looking for love outside of my marriage but having not received any from George, I had no choice if I ever wanted to experience that first-hand. Many nights I could not sleep, kept up by the burning desire for George to love me the way Carlos did. I would often weep as I would lie there alone, feeling my heartbreak for the man I loved so fiercely, but a man who barely seemed to notice me. I knew it was wrong, the guilt forming a pit in my stomach that made me sick, but I was addicted to the high his love gave me. Once I had gotten a taste for it, I could not stop. He would shower me with compliments that made me feel like I was the only girl in the world, like no one else could ever compare and he treated me with the utmost respect; any girl would be lucky to have him. But I could not love him the way I did George; it was just not the same. The part of my heart reserved for George would always be there, an empty gaping hole in my chest that ached, but I would not have it any other way. It was a part of me; I had accepted that.

When George found out about my infidelity a couple of years later, he showed no signs of hurt or betrayal. When he came to me to tell me he knew about my affair, there was a complete lack of emotion.

At the time, I almost snapped. I wanted to grab his head in my hands and shake it, to scream,

"Why can't you just care!" and make him give me an answer. But the feeling of utter defeat that consumed me would not allow me. His reaction made it very clear that I had never had him to begin with, so I did not lose him. He was never mine to lose. I did not even try to argue or protest when he simply collected his belongings and left Italy to move to France in 1824.

The affair became a much-talked-about public scandal in Rome as everyone was aware of my marriage to George Bridgetower, bringing even more attention to the situation as he was a widely known violinist. Carlos's family were horrified that their son, a prince, was having an affair with a married woman. However, like me, his family's disapproval did not seem to bother him.

For the next three years, our affair continued, pausing briefly when George returned to Italy for Christmas in 1827. George's impromptu trip was planned so that he could come to see our daughter as well as planning for a legal separation from me. While he was here, he stayed in the family home alongside Felicity and me. Even after my affair and the fact that I had not seen him for three long years, I could not help but dream about a life with us all together as a family, when I would watch him interact with Felicity. But he only planned to stay until spring.

Just as he was leaving, I once again found out that I was pregnant, this time keeping it to myself. George returned to England, unaware of my pregnancy and filed the papers for a legal separation on 12th May 1828. A little over six months later, I gave birth to a baby boy, and I named him Ludovic Bridgetower. Naturally, there was talk about who the father of my son was, but I paid little attention to the hushed whispers. I knew the truth in my heart of hearts and did not feel the need to prove it to anyone. I knew Carlos was in love with me and that he adored my children, and so long as I could rest easy and be confident in that, it did not matter what the rest of Rome thought. As time went by, his family began to despise me.

They were outraged with the disrespect I brought upon them by going against their customs, me being a married woman with children and him being a prince. He was expected to marry a princess and produce family heirs, even though he had a brother Anthony, who had decided he was never going to take a wife. So, it was down to Carlos as the last remaining heir to commit and they would never have heirs produced by the likes of me. They would make sure of that.

Chapter 17.

Felicity's Story, London

On the 3rd of July, 1835, my mother, Mary Bridgetower died, taking a piece of me with her. Official reports claim her untimely passing was due to suspected food poisoning, but I knew that was untrue. She showed no signs of being ill in the days leading up to her death and then suddenly, she was gone. I was just sixteen years old, and Ludovic was seven. I knew in my heart that the Count's family had something to do with it. They were the only family powerful enough to make this whole scandal disappear and the removal of my mother was the answer.

I heard the way they spoke about her and although I tried to never let it bother me, after the suspicious circumstances of her death, I could not help but take their comments to heart. It could only have been Carlos's family; my reports to the police and the press highlighting the questionable manner of her passing, accusing the family of murdering my mother, and still, no investigations were ever made. Justice for my mother was denied.

After her passing, it was many weeks before my father arrived back in Italy to take care of me and my little brother,

Ludovic. In the run-up to his arrival, my mother's friend, Vittoria, and her husband Louis Mazzara, who ran a boarding house in Rome, were taking care of both of us.

I was distraught. When my father returned to Italy, I was relieved, believing he would take some of the heavy load and would help me get justice for my dear mother. Instead, Carlos came to him and asked if he could take Ludovic to his palace and raise him as his son. Carlos had always loved Ludovic, which stemmed from his still unwavering love for my mother. He had always been good to both of us, treating us as his own and comforting us when other people's cruel words about our mother would weigh heavy on our young souls. While my father had a tender nature with me when I was little, or so I had been told, Ludovic was born after his departure from Italy, so, he never developed a relationship with him, and therefore soon complied with Carlos's request.

I was utterly outraged and at a loss as to how my father could so easily give my little brother to the very people I knew had murdered my mother.

I always knew my father was a cold man from our own extremely limited relationship, but I did not think he was heartless until that point. I could not believe he could be so cruel and so unaffected by my mother's death. Despite them having been separated in the most recent years, they shared several years at each other's side and brought life into this world together. For him to be so callous was insane to me; how could one share all those things without feeling something substantial for the other? This is something I could never forgive him for. He was the cruelest, most unnatural and unfeeling person I had ever met, and I could see that clearly now. The strain on our relationship became so intense that I eventually ran away from our home and stayed with Vittoria and Louis Mazzara to escape. I knew very little about what arrangements my father had put in place before quickly returning to France, but at the time, the less I had to do with him the better; I could barely stand to look at him.

Tragedy seemed to follow me, as Vittoria died of a short illness mere months after my mother. Louis continued to care for me until I reached 21 years of age. After that, I returned to England to sort out my mother's finances as I was the only one able to do so. Louis accompanied me as we had become remarkably close, forming first into a friendship that eventually blossomed into a loving marriage.

My uncle Edward was outraged by my marriage to Louis Mazzara and would not provide the information I needed to access my inheritance, claiming my husband was not a gentleman of property. I could not see how that was supposed to influence my feelings for the man I loved, but Edward felt very strongly about matters of commerce. I also had to get in touch with my father who was living in France, which was no easy task. My pride and unresolved anger were not the only obstacles I had to deal with; we no longer had any communication with one another. In all truth, I had cut off all contact with him, and to keep things fair, he had returned the favor. So, finding him was proving extremely challenging.

In the end, I had to take out a court order against my uncle Edward so that I could claim my inheritance. I pleaded with him to give me a box my mother had left in the family home. It was a heart-shaped casket, set in gold of different colours, with a small key to open it. It contained her hair which she had cut off when she was just slightly younger than I was now. So, of all the things I was entitled to inherit, this was the most precious memory of her now.

My father returned to England after I was finally able to get in contact with him. I had written and told him about the struggles I was facing with my uncle. Although I had not forgiven my father for giving my brother Ludovic to Carlos, or for not showing any sympathy after my mother's death, I needed his help. But I was still filled with anger towards him and consumed with grief.

When I told my Aunt Clara how angry and disgusted I was with my father, she sat me down and began to give me an in-depth insight into his personality, which showed him from a completely different angle, and that changed my entire perception of him.

She told me my father found complete solace in music, but outside of that, he could not express his emotions or empathy the way other people did. This was something my mother had been aware of when they first met; she had told Clara that he was like an unopened book, mysterious and so detached from the world and the people in it.

My mother believed she had the power to change him, simply because she loved him and wanted him to love her back, even moving to Italy to find some peace and tranquility, hoping it would make his love for her as powerful as hers was for him, but it failed and, after several years, she accepted the fact that he was incapable of showing affection the way she wanted him; the way she dreamed of.

Clara went on to tell me that when my father arrived in Italy after my mother's death, he was extremely anxious. When he saw how distraught and broken I was, he did not know how to comfort me and felt there was no merit in him trying, as he could not replace my mother or her love. So, for him, it made sense to stand back.

When Carlos asked to take Ludovic to his palace and rear him as his own child, my father felt it was in Ludovic's best interest. It was the one time in his life he had made a conscious decision about somebody else's life; he knew Carlos loved him dearly as he did my mother.

After my conversation with Clara, I felt sad for not having understood my father sooner and wasting so many years. Letting go of all that anger was liberating and understanding that my father showing his love in different ways by no means diminished it.

I could see why my father was able to have something resembling a tender connection with Clara. Her shy gentle nature seemed to take the pressure off him. It was one of the few relationships he chose to build upon of his own free will, at his own pace, in his own comfort zone.

I returned to Italy with my husband and soon we were blessed with two sons, Felix and Nicholas. My father came out several times to visit us and I worked on building my relationship with him.

Back home in England, my father had moved to Swiss Cottage, Peckham in the county of Surrey. He had maintained a good relationship with Eliza and her two children after his brother died. He was close to his nephew, Freiderike, who had become a professor of music; he had married and had two children of his own. My father was becoming frail and had begun to put his own affairs in order, dividing his estate while he could and making sure that my Uncle Edward was sharing the profits of the estate correctly, but on Tuesday, the 4th of July 1854, he had little choice but to write to his solicitor, Mr. Appleby, Red Lion Square, London, filing a bill of complaint to the Chancery. He named me and my husband Louis, as well as our two sons, Felix and Nicholas, as plaintiffs, while naming my Uncle Edward as the defendant. My father filed this bill after Edward had withdrawn money meant to be shared amongst the family and then disappeared with the money.

Edward was removed as trustee to the estate and restrained from receiving Bank Annuities or Dividends until we could appoint a new Trustee. Until that time, the trusts would be performed and carried out under a decree of the court.

Over the following years, my sons became intrigued with their forefathers and wanted to know where the names Bridgetower and Polgreen came from; they wanted to know as much as possible.

When we returned to England, my sons and my cousin Fredrick and his children would sit with my father for hours and hours, wanting to hear all the stories about our family's history that his father had passed down to him And, like a loving grandfather, he told us all he remembered about our ancestors, telling us first we were descendants of the Solomonic dynasty that dated back hundreds of years in Abyssinia. He explained how our forefathers were sold into slavery, and how his own father managed to escape it.

He told us that when his father, John, was incarcerated in 1802, HRH the Prince of Wales began making regular payments from the royal staff account to his mother, Maria, who lived in Germany. She refused to touch the money saying it would be like betraying her husband and she would never give HRH the pleasure of thinking his money would compensate her husband's wrongful imprisonment. When she died in 1807, the payments continued to be paid into her account, right until 1817 when his father John died age 63. For fifteen years HRH made the regular payments to her account. When no one came forward to claim the money, notices were put in German and British newspapers for Maria Bridgetower's family to come forward to claim the money. No one ever did.

It was wonderful that my father was able to share some of these stories with his grandsons and nephews before he died in 1860. He wanted no gratitude during his life but always assured that the needs of those who needed him were met. I had precious memories to look back on fondly, the same way I did for my mother.

My father, George Polgreen Bridgetower, was laid to rest in a tomb at Kensal Green cemetery in London. What was left from his estate was bequeathed to my Aunt Clara who had moved to Scotland.

After my father's death, his grandsons and nephews became more obsessed with the injustice inflicted upon their forefathers.

Their devotion to proudly claiming their heritage was so intense, that they even went as far as travelling to Abyssinia, and returning to England with incontestable proof that their great-great-grandfather was, in fact, an heir to the Abyssinian throne before he was forced to become a slave for the British Empire.

They contacted Lord Stanley in 1867 hoping for acknowledgment or at least an apology. He reported to British newspapers on the subject and assured the claimant that:

'England will not interfere with the Abyssinian succession, and we suppose Sir Bridgetower vents his wrath against "perfidious England."

Our heritage and customs were regarded as insignificant, but nonetheless, we were proud of our forefathers and our African heritage.

The African kingdom of Abyssinia claimed direct descent from the Solomonic Dynasty and the biblical King Solomon and Makeda, the Queen of Sheba. Their Christian heritage and the establishment of churches, monasteries and castles ensured that the Abyssinian Empire was never to be formally colonised by a European power.

FASILIDES CASTLE

In Gondar, the city emperor Fasilides proclaimed as the Capital of Abyssinia

Lightning Source UK Ltd.
Milton Keynes UK
UKHW020732120820
368104UK00008B/137